The Rockhound's Guide
to TEXAS

by
Melinda Crow

Consulting Editor
W.R.C. Shedenhelm

FALCON™

Falcon Press is continually expanding its list of recreational guidebooks. All books include detailed descriptions, accurate maps, and all information necessary for enjoyable trips. You can order extra copies of this book and get information and prices for other Falcon books by writing Falcon Press, P.O. Box 1718, Helena, MT 59624. Also, please ask for a free copy of our current catalog listing all Falcon Press books.

Caution

Outdoor recreation activities are by their very nature potentially hazardous. All participants in such activities must assume the responsibility for their own actions and safety. The information contained in this guidebook cannot replace sound judgment and good decision-making skills, which help reduce risk exposure, nor does the scope of this book allow for disclosure of all the potential hazards and risks involved in such activities.

Learn as much as possible about the outdoor recreation activities you participate in, prepare for the unexpected, and be safe and cautious. The reward will be a safer and more enjoyable experience.

CONTENTS

ACKNOWLEDGMENTS

This book certainly could not have been written without the help and support of a lot of people. Great thanks to all those veteran rockhounds who looked beyond my naivety to answer questions and point me in the right direction. Thanks must also go to Otis Johnson who renewed my faith in the belief that some of the most beautiful rock treasures in the world are found right here in Texas. (Quite a few of them in his backyard.) While many rock shops would rather sell exotic stones from Brazil or some place most of us will never see, Otis prefers the home-grown stuff, and so do I.

When it comes to teachers, I had two of the greatest. My favorite geologist, Mark Hassell, taught me more about Texas geology than I thought I wanted to know, did a great job of helping with fossil and mineral identification, and never once laughed at my silly questions. Chuck Hassell, photographic genius, probably did laugh at my silly questions, but then he laughs at everything; he's an Aggie. His help with the photos in the book was invaluable. The biggest thanks of all go to my husband Gary and my daughter Alyssa. They endured dusty roads, endless stops, and way too much fast food, all so that I would not have to go alone.

SITE LOCATIONS

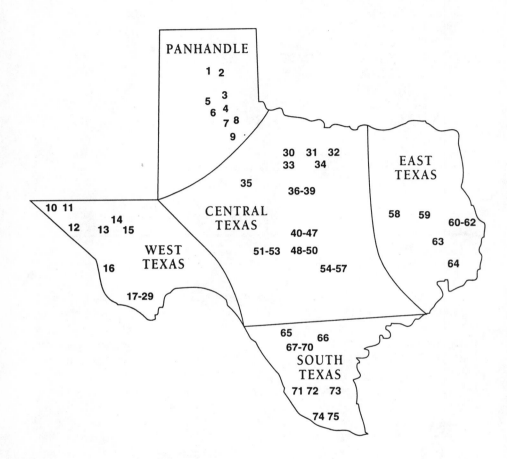

LEGEND

⚒	Rockhound Site		Large Town/City
🏠	Residence or Building	◯	Town
	Road	▲	Mountain Peak
	River	(888)	Interstate
	Dirt Road	(88)	U.S. Highway
	Boundry	88	State Highway
	Dam	88	County or Forest Road
			Lake/Reservoir

The Gallery of Earth Sciences features the Perkins and Ann Sams Collection of gems and minerals. This is kunzite, a pegmatite mineral. Photo courtesy of Natural Science.

ABOUT THIS BOOK

When I was little, my dad used to search the countryside near Amarillo for Phytosaur teeth and arrowheads. When I was a little older, he took me someplace in New Mexico in search of Apache tears. Until I began work on this book, that was the extent of my rockhounding experience.

The expertise I began with was based on extensive travel in Texas. I have spent thirty-three years driving, hiking, and camping across the state. I knew all the possible areas to look, and I knew plenty of people willing to fill my brain with the information I needed.

The challenge before me was to learn a lot about rocks, and spend a lot of time on the road finding them. Simple enough. As a journalist, I undertook the project much as I would any other assignment. What I didn't anticipate was falling in love—with rocks.

In the rock shop at Woodward Ranch, I saw a sign that explained how to tell if you are a rockhound. It seems that first you must buy a bag of marbles. Every time you pick up a rock, you drop a marble. When all your marbles are gone, you're a rockhound. I lost all of mine on the first trip into the field.

Each new road trip was like Christmas morning; each newly discovered site like a gift I didn't expect. But unlike a kid ripping through packages, I never wanted to rush on to the next site. Once a new batch of goodies was revealed, it was difficult to leave it behind in search of others.

The results of my love affair are detailed here. The sites are divided into five regional sections with as many sites in each section as I could find. Some of the sites are widely known places such as Woodward Ranch in West Texas. Others are undocumented, previously known only to any lucky rockhound that stumbled upon them the same way I did.

This is not a book solely about rocks and where to find them, however. It is designed to be a guide to the state of Texas as a rockhound might see it. Obviously, where to find the best rock treasures is an important part of the book, but it isn't the whole thing.

Because the act of collecting rocks brings us in contact with nature, information on the natural surroundings of each site is included. This information is sometimes geological, sometimes biological, and sometimes historical. Information is also included regarding accommodations near each site. Almost all sites listed have motels available within fifty miles, and site listings generally include approximate mileage to the nearest one. Keep in mind, however, that nearest isn't always best, and except in a few cases where a lodge or hotel is of particular interest, no recommendations are made. For recreational vehicle owners, listings include information regarding availability of RV parking near the site.

Introductory information is included regarding wildlife in the state, and the possible threat they may pose. This is critical information to anyone planning to venture beyond the confines of their vehicle in this state. Some site listings also include specific cautions for the immediate area. I did not encounter a single rattlesnake while doing my research, and I wish the same for you. Happy hunting.

Santa Elena Canyon typifies the rugged beauty found throughout the state.

INTRODUCTION

The one word that best describes Texas is "vast." If you could flip the state horizontally on its western tip, it would reach the Pacific Ocean. Flip it toward the east, and El Paso would end up in the Atlantic. Texas' borders encompass 275,416 square miles of mountains, desert, rolling plains, marshland, forest, and beaches. More than 71,000 miles of state highways snake across the state, connecting more than 3,100 cities and towns.

The name Texas comes from the Caddo Indian word Tejas, meaning friends, and Texans take their name seriously. The state motto is even "Friendship." The state bird is the mockingbird, which makes its home in all areas of the state, perched in the state tree: pecan. The state flower, bluebonnet, blooms in April, filling central Texas pastures with its heady scent, and a clear blue that mirrors the sky overhead. That same blue glitters in the state gemstone: blue topaz. The state stone is petrified palmwood.

Though oil and gas production reigns as the state's number one industry, twenty-two minerals are produced commercially, including magnesium, uranium, sulfur, graphite, iron ore, gypsum, salt, and talc. Additionally, pink granite from central Texas is widely used in building materials across the state and the nation. In the past, the mines of West Texas even produced small amounts of silver, lead, and mercury. Tourism in the southern part of the state from "winter Texans" adds to the economy there.

ROCKHOUND TREASURES

For the rockhound, the vastness and variety found in Texas, means an almost endless supply of new treasures to seek. Gemstones like garnet, topaz, and precious opal are found scattered in West and Central Texas. Fossils, large and small, are abundant statewide. Many areas of the state are rich in chalcedony in all forms: agate, flint, jasper, chrysoprase, carnelian, and onyx. Petrified wood can be found throughout the state, a large portion of it is gemstone quality. The possibilities are enough to satisfy the most jaded hunter. The best news is that the caches are often found concentrated in relatively small areas. Because of this, many a rockhound finds his niche in one part of the state, and never feels the need to look elsewhere.

THE LANDSCAPE

The terrain of the state defies easy description. The far western portion of the state includes both the northern reaches of the Chihuahuan Desert and the southern tip of the Rocky Mountains. The eastern edge of the state borders on the swampland of Louisiana. The territory that lies in between is quite diverse, as is the weather. Annual precipitation ranges from an average of fifty-nine inches along the Sabine River to less than eight inches in the western desert regions. And while 90-plus-degree temperatures prevail statewide during the summer months, winter brings a wide range of chill factors. The southern portions of the state remain mild throughout most of the winter months. But just a few hundred miles to the north, the Panhandle spends the winter shivering under a blast of Canadian wind. Even people as far north as Midland consider themselves lucky not to have to endure the frigid winters of Lubbock and Amarillo.

Six broad geographical descriptions can be used to divide the state. The northern portion of the state is called the Panhandle. Elevations average around 3,300 feet, but at the eastern boundary of the area (an eroded escarpment known as the Caprock) the elevation drops quickly to around 2,300 feet. Broken only by a few areas of eroded canyons (like Palo Duro Canyon, near Amarillo) and valleys, this region aptly earns the name "High Plains." The flat land with fertile soil is ideal for farming and cattle grazing. Herds of antelope, though not as great in number as in the past, roam the wide open spaces. Coyotes, rattlesnakes, and rabbits are in abundant supply.

Although the Panhandle is the northernmost area on the map, it is never referred to as "North Texas." That designation is reserved for the area southeast of the Panhandle, bordered by eastern Oklahoma and southwestern Arkansas. With mean elevations that drop to around 400 feet near the Arkansas border, the gently rolling prairies of North Texas are dotted with man-made and natural lakes. Small-scale agriculture abounds in and around the numerous oil fields, and native vegetation is thick and lush. With the Dallas-Ft. Worth metroplex at its heart, this is the most heavily populated region of the state. With the exception of scattered fossil sites, the area holds few rock treasures.

The least populous portion of the state lies southwest of the Panhandle: the arid basin and mountain area of West Texas known as the Trans-Pecos. Because grasses grow sparsely here, ranches are often necessarily large, with fewer cattle per acre or, as some ranchers say, more acres per cow. The chief industry here is oil, but jack rabbits outnumber both pump jacks and people. The area contains ninety-one peaks that are a mile high or more. The state's highest, Guadalupe Peak (8,749 feet) is found near the New Mexico border.

Farther south, Big Bend National Park encompasses the multi-colored Chisos Range. The park is bordered to the south by two hundred-foot stone cliffs etched by the Rio Grande River. Wildlife in West Texas comes in numerous shapes and sizes. Mountain lions, bobcats, and bear roam here in addition to the standard Texas fare of deer, coyotes, and rattlers. Plume agate in numerous colors is the number one rockhound goal here, but gemstones and petrified woods are also found in large quantities throughout the region.

The Central Texas landscape is one of moderate hills surrounded by relatively level, oak-dotted savannah. At the center of the region is the Llano Uplift area, north of San Antonio. This gently arched rise offers glimpses of Precambrian granite and gneiss throughout the region. Many of the state's best gemstone deposits are found in this area. Elevations range from 1,800 feet near San Angelo to a mere 700 feet at San Antonio.

Post oak, mesquite, and cedar are scattered across the landscape. The highlands offer abundant grasslands suitable for sheep and goats, including exotics like angoras. Along with rattlesnakes and rabbits, wildlife here also includes an over-abundant supply of deer. In many locales, the seasonal influx of deer hunters provides a necessary boon to the economy. Because of this, rock hunters should never venture off main roads any time from October through January. Further information about hunting seasons statewide can be obtained from the Texas Parks and Wildlife Department, 4200 Smith School Road, Austin, Texas 78744, 1-800-792-1112.

As the elevation of the hill country drops, the rolling plains give way to some of Texas' flattest territory: the Coastal Plains, which is located in the southern tip of the state. Made up of layer upon layer of mud and sand washed here by rivers headed for the Gulf of Mexico, the northern areas of this region are a prime target for rockhounds looking for petrified woods. It is bounded on the east by pine forests (including four national forests) and on the west by the fertile Rio Grand Valley. Elevations here slope gently from around 400 feet at Laredo, down to sea level at the Gulf. Manufacturing, shipping, and tourism are prime industries along the 624 miles of coastline, but farming, cattle ranching, and forestry also contribute heavily to the economy of the area.

At the far eastern edge of the state, flat grasslands quickly change to dense forests. Timber is the number one industry in the region; even the four national forests are harvested by clear cutting and replanting. One word describes the weather in East Texas: wet. Annual rainfall averages from fifty to sixty inches per year. As one might guess, petrified wood, particularly palm wood is the main rock hounding target, but other finds include tektites, fossils, and jasper.

SIGHTS TO SEE

MUSEUMS AND SPECIAL DISPLAYS

Texas counties seem to abide by an unwritten code of one museum minimum per county, and almost every one of them has rocks on display. Time permitting, they can be a good source of information when in unknown territory. There are a few really good exhibits that are worth making time for, however.

The premier gem and mineral exhibit in the state is found at the Houston Museum of Natural Science in the Lillie and Roy Cullen Gallery of Earth Science. The gallery is home to the collection of Perkins and Ann Sams of Midland. When the Sams set out to build the collection, the goal was to only have the best of the best. There are many who believe they put together the finest collection in the world. Lucky for Texas that one stipulation they placed on the collection was that it must remain in the state. The Houston museum raised the money to purchase the collection so that this would be possible.

Rather than simply line up the stones in rows of square glass cases, the museum chose to match the mood of the gallery with the drama of the stones. In places visitors get the feeling they have ventured underground to view the treasures hidden below. It has been said that after viewing the first room, the second and third rooms almost seem like overkill, so breathtaking is the beauty of the collection. It probably wasn't a rockhound who said it though. The museum is located in Hermann Park, and is open Sunday and Monday from noon to 5 p.m., and Tuesday through Saturday from 9 a.m. to 5 p.m.

Midland is home to the Permian Basin Petroleum Museum, where visitors can explore the world of petroleum from the inside out. A walk through a mock-up of the Permian Sea as it looked 230 million years ago provides useful insight to fossil hunters. While the focus of the museum is on the mechanics of the oil industry, exhibits also provide detailed information on geological formations across the state. It's a worthwhile educational for even the most experienced Texas rockhound. Indian artifacts, fossils and rock specimens are displayed as well. The museum is located on Interstate 20 west of town and is open 9 a.m. to 5 p.m. Monday through Saturday and 2 p.m. to 5 p.m. Sunday.

CAVES
Because the hobby of rock collecting involves so much more than simply picking up pretty rocks on the ground, collectors are usually intrigued by almost anything relating to the earth and its past. Caves can provide a fascinating means of learning from the inside out. Fortunately, in Texas, dabbling into the realm of spelunking requires no special gear and no crawling around in the dark. Central Texas is home to numerous caves and caverns where weary rockhounds can find an underground change of pace, complete with paved trails, lights, and guided tours.

One of the best in the state is the Caverns of Sonora. Described by some as "the most beautiful cave in the world," the cave features spectacular butterfly formations, delicate "soda straw" formations several feet long, and bridges that cross black crevices of undetermined depth. The tour guides are well-informed regarding the geology of the cave and how the various formations develop. Cameras are encouraged, but touching is not allowed since many of the formations are still growing. The caverns are located just south of Sonora off of Interstate Highway 10. A gift and rock shop is located at the entrance. A nice RV park complete with hookups and hungry peacocks is located at the cavern as well.

In the San Antonio area, Natural Bridge Caverns is worth stopping for. The cave is filled with thousands of formations, including the interesting and somewhat rare "fried eggs." Other caves in the area that are open to the public include Longhorn Caverns, Inner Space Cavern, Cascade Caverns, Wonder World, Cave Without A Name, and Kickapoo Caverns.

PARKS

The Texas Parks and Wildlife Department operates more than one hundred parks scattered throughout the state. Many offer camping with electricity and water and hot water showers. All are just about guaranteed to bring you a little closer to nature. The beauty and amenities found in the parks make them an ideal place for RVs. It is important to remember, however, that no collecting is allowed in any state park.

Palo Duro Canyon is the largest state park. Nicknamed "the Grand Canyon" of Texas, it often comes as quite a shock to those who have never seen it. One minute you're driving across the flat prairie wondering just where this darn canyon is; the next you're staring in awe at a yawning expanse of multi-colored cliffs towering over the canyon bottom. It is a sight not to be missed if you're in the Panhandle.

Carved by the Prairie Dog Town Fork of the Red River, the canyon allows the opportunity to view much of the geology of the High Plains in cross section. Rocks from four different geological periods are represented: Permian, Triassic, Upper Tertiary, and Quaternary. Unfortunately, the canyon doesn't present a complete picture geologically. What nature giveth, nature can also taketh away. Erosion has completely erased evidence of Jurassic, Cretaceous, or Lower Tertiary periods within the canyon walls.

The rocks that are present, though, offer more than enough to keep most rock enthusiasts happy. Because collecting is prohibited inside the state park, the adventure through the canyon is best treated as a learning expe-

Camping at Palo Duro Canyon offers a close-up look at the geology of the area.

rience. The geological lessons learned here can prove tremendously useful when scouring the rest of the Panhandle for treasure.

Starting at the bottom, the canyon floor and the lowest formation visible in the canyon walls is the Quartermaster Formation of Permian aged rocks. They are red shales layered with gray shales, mudstones, clays, and sandstones. Also layered within this formation are veins of gypsum.

Three forms of gypsum are found in the canyon. The most common is satin spar. It is slightly fibrous and forms in thin white bands. Selenite is also present. It is colorless, crystalline, and is usually formed in sheet-like masses. The third variety is alabaster. It is in granular form, is generally white, but occasionally tinged or streaked with rose and pale pink as the result of impurities. Massive boulders of the alabaster can be found both inside the canyon, and in some surrounding areas.

Rocks from the Triassic period are seen overlying the Quartermaster Formation. The lavender, gray, white, and orange shales and sandstones are a part of the Tecovas formation. Of interest to the rockhound in this formation are fossils, namely Phytosaur teeth and bones, petrified wood, and coprolites. This formation is also the place to look for concretions and geodes.

The next formation is the Trujillo. Consisting mainly of a massive bed of tough sandstone. This is the rock from which the rugged cliffs are formed. In many places it acted as a sturdy capstone which refuses to give in to erosion, even when the softer soils beneath it crumble and slip toward the canyon floor, thus forming the interesting towers and pedestals seen throughout the canyon.

The uppermost formation in the canyon is the Ogalala of Upper Tertiary rocks. This formation consists of medium-grained sandstone and gravels, topped by a thick layer of caliche. The gravels of this formation most likely were laid down as the result of erosion from the nearby Rocky Mountains. Found within the mixture are fragments of petrified wood, small agates, flint, jasper, and very colorful quartzite pebbles.

All these rocks and not one to take home! It is probably the most difficult challenge a rockhound must face when visiting Palo Duro Canyon. But any hound worth anything knows the importance of leaving some things just as they are. Take heart though, included in this book are site listings which should guide you to all of the same treasures outside the park.

Other state parks of special interest to rockhounds are Caprock Canyons near Quitaque, Copper Breaks near Quanah, Dinosaur Valley near Glen Rose, Enchanted Rock near Fredericksburg, Hueco Tanks near El Paso, Monahans Sandhills near Monahans, and Seminole Canyon near Langtry.

Hounds just looking for a scenic stopover will find state parks like Davis Mountains, Fort Parker, Guadalupe River, Kerrville, Mustang Island, and Palmetto to their liking. For those that enjoy water-related activities, thirty-eight of the state parks offer lakes with boat ramps.

In addition to the state parks, Texas has four national forests, two national monuments, two national recreation areas, three national historical

The pink granite dome of Enchanted Rock rises above the Texas hill country.

sites, one national preserve, one national seashore, and two national parks.

The smaller of the two parks is Guadelupe Mountains National Park. It contains 76,293 acres of rugged mountains at the southern end of the Rockies. Elevations range from 3,650 to 8,749 feet atop the state's highest point, Guadelupe Peak. The park encompasses eighty miles of marked hiking trails, which provide the bulk of the access to the interior of the park. This is not the place to give mountain hiking a first-time try however. Only experienced, well-equipped hikers should venture deep into this unforgiving wilderness.

Two hundred miles southeast of the Guadelupe mountains lies the massive Big Bend National Park. The park encompasses 708,221 acres of desert, mountains, and canyons. The scenery is like none other found in the state. The combined splendor of the rugged mountains and the untamed desert give the park a unique brand of beauty. There are more than 100 miles of paved roads, 175 miles of grated dirt roads, and several hundred miles of hiking trails coursing through the park. Many of the hiking trails are excellent for the novice hiker.

One of the most exquisite hikes is into the mouth of Santa Elena Canyon. The 0.75-mile trail leads you up the edge of canyon walls, and back down to the banks of the Rio Grande. The hike is listed as strenuous in most guides due to the incline, but stone steps and handrails ease the way. (The author's daughter made this hike with no difficulty when she was barely four.)

Accommodations in the park include rooms at the Chisos Mountains Lodge, located in the Basin area of the park. It is heavily booked during winter and spring peak seasons, so reservations are necessary. Phone 915-477-2291. Twenty-five campsites with water, electricity, and sewer can be found at the Rio Grande Village. Sites are on a first come, first served basis, with no reservations taken. Just outside the park at Study Butte, RV parking and motel rooms are plentiful.

For a complete guide to accommodations and recreation in this area, write for a free copy of the Big Bend Area Travel Guide, P.O. Box 401, Alpine, Texas 79831. Phone 915-837-2326.

Please remember that though the mineral offerings are vast at both national parks, no collecting is allowed in either.

TEXAS WILDLIFE

Any adventure that takes place outdoors brings you in the path of creatures of various sizes and shapes. The problem for Texas rockhounds is that a few of these creatures don't always remember the state motto of "Friendship." Occasionally though, the problem is over friendliness, as in the case of a fifty-pound raccoon that thinks he owns eating rights to everything in your camp. With a little caution and the advice that follows, collectors will find that rock hunting alongside the wildlife in Texas is as safe as any place else.

SNAKES

The snake most people worry about when traveling in the western United States is the diamondback rattlesnake. Large populations of the rattler can be found in all regions of Texas, with the greatest concentrations located west of a line drawn from Ft. Worth to Corpus Christi. (This area encompasses more than half the state.) Because of this, collectors should never venture out without a snake bite kit. Know how to use it and test the suction device periodically to ensure that it works properly. Obviously, the best approach would be to avoid a confrontation in the first place, so a little knowledge of the habits and lifestyles of the beast is the best defense.

Contrary to popular belief, the rattlesnake does not love extremely hot weather. In fact, their levels of activity peak at around 80 to 85 degrees Fahrenheit. What that means to the collector, is that early morning or late evening expeditions during the warm months require extra caution. Summer daytime heat usually finds the rattler sleeping under the cover of rock ledges or brush, so care is necessary around these areas. Winter rock hunting, though considerably safer, still requires a certain amount of vigilance because temperatures in many parts of the state remain moderate. This allows the rattler to make brief appearances from his den to bask in the winter sun.

When spring arrives, the snakes are most active. It is during this season that they must eat more to replace weight lost during the winter, and provide energy for mating. A word of caution regarding the youngsters which are born in late summer: They often are easier to anger, less experienced at remaining undetected (making confrontations more likely), and have less control over the amount of venom injected into a bite. In other words, be particularly watchful of smaller snakes.

Texas also has two other varieties of poisonous snakes to be considered: the Western cottonmouth water moccasin and the copperhead moccasin. Though not as deadly, nor as easily angered as the rattler, a wide berth should be given any snake discovered while collecting.

MAMMALS

Mammals found in the Texas countryside include thousands of species, but those most commonly encountered are rabbits, raccoons, deer, armadillo, and coyotes. Obviously the deer and the rabbits pose no threat. The armadillo looks like a cross between a giant rat and a lizard, but also presents no danger to rockhounds (or anyone else for that matter). They are nocturnal and occasionally work their way into campsites during their nightly foraging for insects and berries.

Because they are often carriers of rabies, raccoons are best avoided when possible. Daytime collectors will have no difficulty doing this, but overnight camping presents a challenge. Anything that smells should be stored in difficult-to-open containers. Really difficult. Raccoons have been known to open ice chests, fishing tackle boxes and even trailer doors. The best practice is to remove all temptation by keeping foodstuffs locked inside a vehicle at night.

Coyotes are usually not difficult to avoid. They are generally more afraid of people than we are of them. The only time one might pose a threat to a human is under stressful circumstances such as disease or injury, or in the case of a mother protecting her pups. Should one cross your path, never attempt to get a closer look. Simply make some loud noises or throw rocks to send it on its way.

OTHER PESTS

The greatest outdoor nuisance to rockhounds (and everybody else for that matter) in Texas is likely to be the huge population of insects and their kin. The western half of the state has scorpions, tarantulas, and biting flies. The eastern half has chiggers and mosquitoes, and ticks are a problem statewide. As if all that weren't enough, along come Africanized honey bees.

The so called "killer bees" arrived in South Texas from Mexico in the early 1990s and are slowly migrating north. The bees earned their reputation because of a tendency to swarm in masses, and anyone caught in the swarm is likely to suffer multiple stings. The sting is no more deadly than that of native honey bees, but allergic reactions are equally possible. As of this writing, only one fatality has been attributed to the bees in Texas. That death was the result of an attempt to smoke the bees out of a hive in a vacant building. Entomologists advise that no attempts should be made to disturb any honey bee colony in the state without the supervision of a qualified exterminator. Most rockhounds aren't likely to go around stirring up bee hives, but because the bees swarm easily, care should be taken to avoid all bee colonies.

Despite their reputation, tarantulas and scorpions are rarely deadly. Tarantulas seem inclined to mind their own business, and will simply run when disturbed. Scorpions, which inflict a painful sting, are somewhat more difficult to avoid due to their pale tan coloring, which blends quite well with rocks and tent floors. Overnight campers in the area would be well advised to check shoes before putting them on in the morning.

As for the smaller nuisances of ticks and chiggers, the best prevention is the practice of wearing long pants tucked into boots with a light spray of insect repellent over all clothing. A little advance preparation and common sense goes a long way with all of these pests.

The intent of this discussion of potentially worrisome wildlife was not to discourage rockhounds from venturing into the Texas wilderness, but rather to better prepare them for any possibility. Rock hunting in Texas is usually not as simple as a stroll through the park, and a healthy dose of respect for the creatures of the land is a prerequisite.

KIDS AND ROCKS

Today's children live in a world where Christmas trees are made of plastic, and anybody they see on television might qualify as a hero. They are surrounded by technology that makes life easier but leads them away from the natural world with the speed of an electrical impulse in a fiber-optic cable. There are children whose only contact with nature is what they see on Public Broadcasting Service.

It's a "Catch-22" situation, however. Because technology is today's reality, today's kids must embrace the science upon which the wizardry is founded if they are to be able to survive in tomorrow's world. What is science? Very simply, it is the study of the world around us. What better place to begin to understand the world, and thus science, than with the rocks under their feet?

Rockhounding is a hobby with close ties to geology, chemistry, physics, archeology, geography, and paleontology. The process of mineral identification builds necessary research and observation skills. It takes kids out of the classroom, away from the computer and the TV screen, and puts them back in touch with nature.

Collecting rocks is a natural even for pre-school age children. Kids are attracted to small, colorful objects they can claim as their own. Rocks are everywhere, and it takes only a small amount of encouragement and teaching from an adult to get kids to look beyond pebbles in the backyard.

There are a few things to keep in mind when rockhounding with children. The first is to refrain from criticism of that backyard pebble collection. Teach gently without offering your own personal opinions regarding color, size, quality, or quantity. Remember that it's their collection. So what if they only like black rocks? Help them discover as many varieties of black rocks as possible.

It is important when taking children into the field to choose sites that are appropriate to the age of the child. Accessibility is the real measure here. A two-mile hike through the deserts of West Texas lugging water may seem like a grand adventure to a twelve-year-old experienced hiker, but a nightmare to a five-year-old. Sites should also be selected for their success ratio. There should be something neat to take home from almost every site visited with children.

Teaching rockhounding safety and ethics is as important as teaching where to look for what. Children must be made aware of snake avoidance practices before that first trip into the field. They should be taught the importance of safety goggles, good hiking boots, sunscreen and drinking water.

A little gentle teaching is all that is required when children express an interest in rock collecting.

Most importantly, as we share the joy of this fascinating hobby with the younger generation, we must teach them that it is sometimes better to leave more than we take. And along with nurturing their passion for collecting the beauties of the earth, we should instill in them the responsibility to preserve these natural treasures.

GEM AND MINERAL SHOWS

Rough rocks, polished rocks, faceted gemstones, fossils, jewelry, lapidary equipment, rockhounds, wholesalers, retailers, and a few people who didn't have a clue what they were getting into when they walked through the door. You'll encounter all of this at the many gem and mineral shows held across the state.

While miniature in comparison to the giant shows held in other parts of the country (like Arizona), these shows will whet your appetite and satisfy you until you can make it to Tucson. Here is a sampling of the Texas shows:

City	Site	Month Usually Held
Amarillo	Civic Center	May
Arlington	Convention Center	July
Austin	Palmer Auditorium	November
Corpus Cristi	Convention Center	March
Fredericksburg	Lady Bird Johnson	January
Houston	Houston Astrodome	June
Lubbock	Civic Center	April
Lajitas	Pavilion	November
Odessa	Ector County Colliseum	March
Pharr	Civic Center	January
San Antonio	Freeman Coliseum	March
Waco	Convention Center	April

ROCKHOUND RULES

Simply finding a site to collect in Texas is often more difficult than actually finding the rocks once you get to the site. The bulk of property in the state is privately owned. The small remainder is almost entirely enclosed in state and national parks and recreation areas. Collecting within state parks, state recreation areas, and national parks is strictly prohibited.

One other possibility to keep in mind is along navigable rivers. The land is public, and collecting for hobby purposes is allowed. Obtaining access to the rivers is the only problem. Remember that trespassing while getting to the river is still trespassing.

Roadside collecting often provides the best means of sampling the rocks available in any particilar area. If your finds leave you wanting more, the next step would be obtaining permission to collect on private property. Ranchers are usually willing to allow a single rockhound or a small group to collect.

When collecting along any road keep a few rules in mind:

- Park well off of the road, and always in sight of oncoming traffic. Even parking on a shoulder is dangerous when your vehicle is obscured by curves or hills.
- Do not attempt to cross any fences or fence lines. Open gates, walk-overs, and cattleguards are not invitations to trespass.
- No overnight camping is allowed beside any highway.
- Collecting should be limited to small samples, with very little digging or chiseling.
- No collecting of plant material is allowed.

Safe parking often requires a walk back to many roadside sites.

THE PANHANDLE

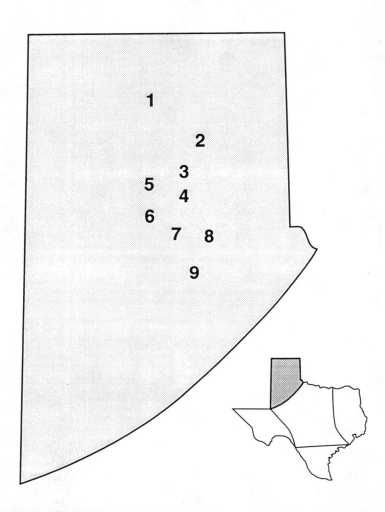

OVERVIEW

The area of the state known as the Panhandle is a choice collecting site for anyone looking for small pieces suitable for tumbling, but larger material is also available. The flint found in this region is unsurpassed in richness and variety of color. Wonderful agatized and opalized woods are also in large supply. Arrowheads are commonly found in the area, as are Phytosaur teeth and Triassic era bones. Lower Cretaceous fossils are found at the southern edges of the Panhandle, and geodes can often be found in the canyon lands with some persistent looking in the right places.

Most collecting in the Panhandle is easily accomplished at roadside sites, or in accessible river beds. Because the land is heavily utilized for farming and cattle grazing, there are very few off-road sites available to the public.

The weather in this area is highly unpredictable. It has been known to snow in May, and to be eighty degrees in January. Summer temperatures often rise to near 100 degrees F. Unexpected storms and cool winds can make spring collecting quite uncomfortable, and risky when collecting is done in low-lying riverbeds. Winter is usually just "down-right" cold. That leaves fall as the most desirable season when the temperatures are usually moderate, the winds are mild, and the rattlesnake population is beginning to settle in for the winter hybernation.

Bird hunting is prevalent in the area. Quail season runs from the end of October through the end of February. Pheasant season is in mid-December. Deer and aoudad sheep are also hunted in some counties from November through January. Rockhounds should be aware of hunting seasons and avoid any collecting other than from main highways at those times.

SITE 1 *ALIBATES NATIONAL MONUMENT*

Land type: Plains/canyons.

Elevation: 3,200 feet.

Best season: Fall.

Land manager: National Parks Department Lake Meredith National Recreation Area, P.O. BOX 1460, Fritch, Texas 79036; (806)857-3151.

Material: No Collecting allowed.

Tools: None.

Vehicle: Any.

Accommodations: Motels, RV sites within 20 miles.

Special attractions: Lake Meredith, Lake Meredith Aquatic And Wildlife Museum in Fritch.

Finding the site: The Alibates quarries are approximately thirty-eight miles north of Amarillo. From U.S. Highway 60 east (Amarillo Blvd.) in Amarillo turn north onto Texas Highway 136 and go toward the town of Fritch. A directional sign indicates the road to the monument approximately thirty-six miles later. Turn west on the monument road; go about three miles to a fork in the road. Take the right fork to reach the monument.

Rockhounding: Flint from Alibates has been prized by collectors for more than 12,000 years. Colors include pink, purple, blue, brown, white, gray, red, and black. Collecting is no longer allowed at the site, but the trip is worthwhile to collectors interested in archeology, history, or those who can successfully look but not touch.

Tributaries to the Canadian River etch across the flat landscape of the Texas Panhandle. The cliffs and bluffs resulting from years of erosion are

SITE 1   ALIBATES NATIONAL MONUMENT

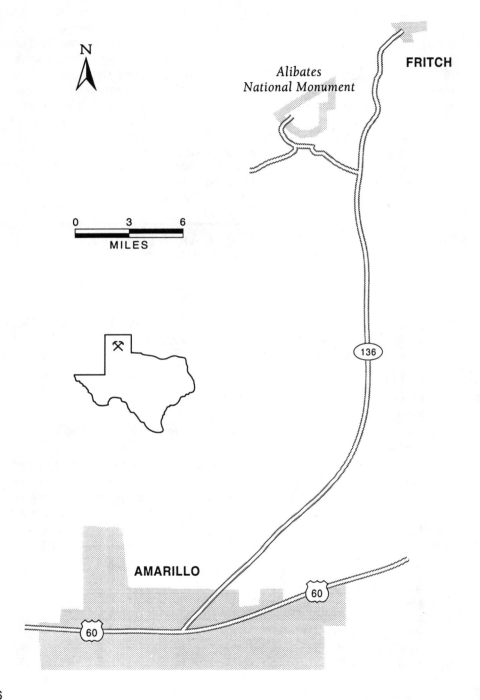

referred to locally as "The Breaks." At these breaks other materials, such as the flint, often hide in the layers of red soil. The flint at Alibates is a byproduct of silica replacement of the dolomite caprock. The result is the fine-grained quartz commonly called chert or flint.

Flint from Alibates litters most of Texas and has been found as far away as Montana in the form of arrowheads and spearpoints. The Alibates National Monument contains more than five hundred quarries and Indian campsites. Evidence points to the use of the flint by man as early as the Ice Age, and as late as 1870. Visits to the quarries are by guided tour only. Make advance reservations by calling the park superintendent at 806-857-3151.

The monument is adjacent to the Lake Meredith National Recreation Area. The lake lies in a two hundred-foot canyon carved by the Canadian River. Construction on the Sanford Dam began in 1962, creating a reliable water source for eleven Panhandle cities, and one of the most popular recreation sites in the area.

SITE 2 *ALANREED RIVER ROCKS*

Land type: Rolling plains.

Elevation: 2,812 feet.

Best season: Fall.

Land manager: Texas Department of Transportation.

Material: Jasper, flint, feldspar, mica.

Tools: Shovels.

Vehicle: Any.

Accommodations: RV park in Alanreed, motel within 20 miles.

Special attraction: Alibates National Monument.

Finding the site: Alanreed is approximately fifty-five miles east of Amarillo, on Interstate 40. From I-40 in Alanreed turn north on Farm Road 291. Travel 2.7 miles north. Look for a gravely road cut on the east side of the road. The road is two lanes, with hills and curves obscuring visibility by oncoming motorists. Safe parking is therefore some distance away.

Rockhounding: Jasper and an unusual mixture of fist-sized, colorful quartzite stones, many with mica inclusions can be found in an out-of-the-way road cut near Alanreed. This cache of gravel and river rocks also contains multi-colored flint chips from the nearby Alibates quarries. Feldspar pebbles are also a common find.

The cobbles found here are part of the Ogallala sand and gravel bed. This wedge-shaped formation was deposited more than 4 million years ago. It lies on the eastern edge of the Rockies, spreading from Texas to Montana. The Alanreed site appears to be a cut and fill channel from a long-ago river or wash.

Nearby Lake McClellan offers similar glimpses of the Ogalala rocks, as

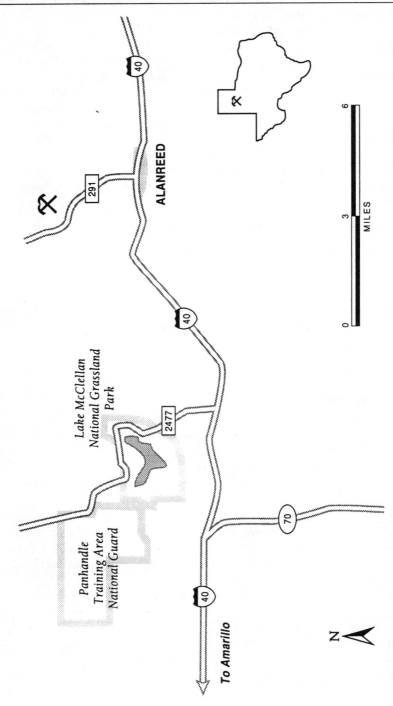

well as occasional finds of Indian artifacts. Though the lake is man-made, McClellan Creek long provided water for anyone traveling across the region. The area below the dam offers the best collecting site for flint. The route to the lake is well marked. From Interstate 40, approximately forty-eight miles east of Amarillo, turn east onto Farm Road 2477.

SITE 3 *GREENBELT RESERVOIR DOLOMITE*

Land type: Rolling plain, river breaks.

Elevation: 2,727 feet.

Best season: Fall.

Land manager: Texas Department of Transportation.

Materials: Dolomite, alabaster.

Tools: Pick, chisel, hammer.

Vehicle: Any.

Accommodations: RV parking at the lake, motels within 20 miles.

Special attraction: Greenbelt Reservoir.

Finding the site: Clarendon is located on U.S. Highway 287, fifty-one miles southeast of Amarillo. In Clarendon turn north on Texas Highway 70. The lake entrance is approximately 5.5 miles north on this road. The best area for collecting dolomite and alabaster is on TX 70, at 0.5 mile north of the lake entrance. Look for the white-topped red cliffs east of the dam. Be careful not to cross any fences onto private property.

Rockhounding: Large specimens of carving-grade dolomite, often with gray-black manganese dendrites, top the bluffs above Greenbelt Reservoir. Also found here is a selection of alabaster with the same interesting inclusions. The two are distinguished by hardness. The alabaster has a hardness of only one to two on the Mohs scale, making it fingernail scratchable, with a powdery feel. The dolomite will have a hardness in the range of three or four, and requires a knife to break the surface. Both types of rock break easily from the cliff side with hammer and chisel.

Both materials are excellent for beginning lapidary work. Because of its softness, the alabaster is ideal for artistic hand-carving. The dolomite lends itself well to machining. It cuts smoothly, and polishes to a pearly luster.

The dolomite is a replacement of calcite by limestone, and lies on top of the red Permian sandstone beds. The nearby Salt Fork of the Red River has eroded away the lighter colored Ogalala soils, leaving the red breaks. The alabaster is a granular form of gypsum commonly found with dolomite.

Greenbelt Reservoir has 1,990 acres of surface water, providing an excellent recreational facility for the area. Unlike many of the Panhandle lakes, Greenbelt isn't a canyon lake. This fact makes it popular with campers and boaters who have easier access to the shoreline here than at Meredith or MacKenzie.

SITE 3   GREENBELT RESERVOIR DOLOMITE

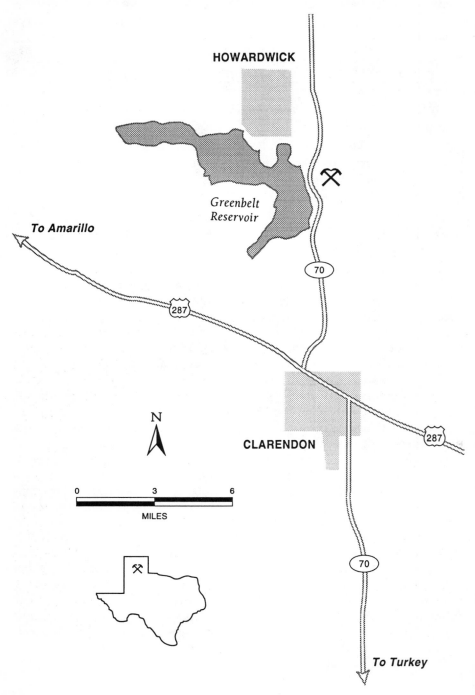

The collecting site near the dam is brushy and the rocky cliffs provide a better than average home for rattlers. An unusual threat to collectors is also found here: bee hives. Honey bees (native variety) have made their home in small cracks and crevices along the cliff nearest the road. Unfortunately, the usual safety precautions applied to snakes won't be of much use against the bees. Careful observation of the area before collecting is highly advised.

SITE 4 *OGALALA GRAVELS NEAR CLARENDON*

Land type: River breaks, canyons.

Elevation: 2,727 feet.

Best season: Fall.

Land manager: Texas Department of Transportation.

Material: Colored quartzite pebbles, jasper, flint, agatized wood, opalized wood,manganese nodules, feldspar.

Tools: None.

Vehicle: Any.

Accommodations: Motels in Clarendon.

Special attraction: Greenbelt Reservoir.

Finding the site: Clarendon is fifty-one miles southeast of Amarillo on U.S. Highway 287. In Clarendon turn south on Texas Highway 70. Exposed

Large chunks of petrified wood like this one found in the Panhandle are often difficult to distinguish from fossil bones.

SITE 4 *OGALALA GRAVELS NEAR CLARENDON*

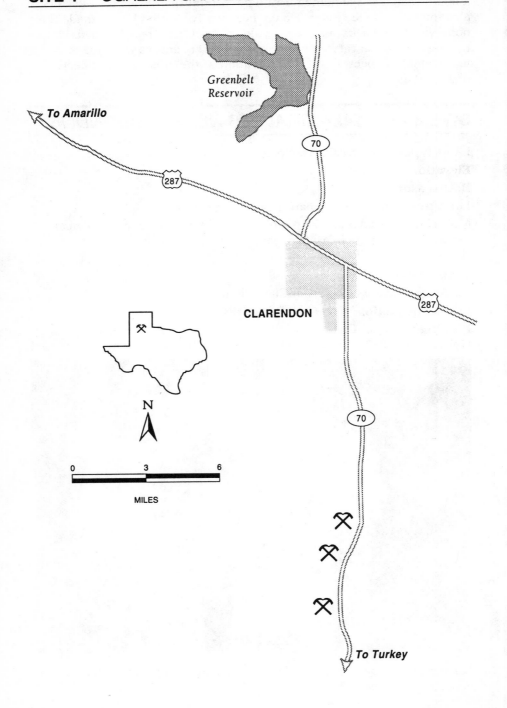

To Amarillo

Greenbelt
Reservoir

70

287

CLARENDON

287

N

0   3   6

MILES

70

To Turkey

gravel beds begin appearing on both sides of the road at approximately seven miles south of Clarendon. They continue for the next two miles.

Rockhounding: Ever look at a *Where's Waldo* book? If you enjoyed it, this site's for you. An interesting mix of highly colorful quartzite pebbles, jasper, agatized wood, opalized wood, pink feldspar, and hollowed out manganese nodules can be found in several road cuts south of Clarendon. The pieces range in size from tiny slivers to fist-sized cobbles. Like searching for Waldo, finding the best pieces takes patience because these gravel beds are extensive.

While most of the stones are likely to lend themselves nicely to tumbling, some of the larger specimens, particularly the woods, make interesting cabochons. Most of the wood found at the site will likely be agatized, that is, a product of purely silica replacement. These stones will cut and polish much the same as any agate. While not as common among the gravels, examples of opalized wood have also been found here. These pieces are hydrous silica replacements, and are therefore more brittle than the agatized woods. Careful attention can produce pieces with great intensity and color.

The beds are a portion of the Ogalala sand and gravel beds that lie at the eastern base of the Rockies. The materials found in the mixture are quite varied. Any given stone may have originated thousands of miles away from the one lying next to it. The erosive effects of the tributaries to the Prairie Dog Fork of the Red River exposed the beds near Clarendon. As the elevation drops farther south, the familiar red Permian rocks appear in the road cuts. Once you reach the red beds, the gravel disappears and the rocks in the road cuts are approximately 200 million years older.

As with all roadside collecting, remember not to cross fences onto private property. This is cattle country, and most land owners take trespassing quite seriously. Any fence climbing could find you at the county courthouse, or worse yet, at the wrong end of a shotgun.

SITE 5 *PALO DURO GEODES*

Land type: Canyons.
Elevation: 2,653 feet.
Best season: Fall.
Land manager: Armstrong, Donley, and Briscoe counties.
Material: Geodes, petrified wood.
Tools: Hammer, shovel.
Vehicle: Utility.
Accommodations: Motels within 20 miles.
Special attractions: Palo Duro Canyon State Park, Caprock Canyons State Park.
Finding the sites: Take U.S. Highway 287 for 6.8 miles southeast of

Claude to Farm Road 2889. Turn south. Approximately four miles later, the pavement ends, and the road becomes County Road 22. This road crosses a narrow inlet off the main canyon. An excellent creek crossing with exposed gravel beds is found approximately four miles after the pavement ends.

Good collecting is also found on an unmarked county road that extends west from Texas Highway 70/256. These two highways are joined for about ten miles between the towns of Turkey and Clarendon. Two miles south of the northern split turn west onto the unmarked dirt road. Bear to the left to avoid short private roads. Excellent roadside collecting areas begin approximately seven miles west of TX 70/256.

The same road splits in southwestern Donley county. The eastern route goes to Clarendon; the western route meets up with Farm Road 2272 southeast of Claude. The road toward Claude presents the best collecting opportunities as it winds toward the bluffs at the canyon edge.

Rockhounding: Visiting the Panhandle and seeing only the portion of Palo Duro Canyon that is encompassed by the state park is like traveling thirty miles to an ice cream store for a single scoop of vanilla; you miss the really good stuff. For a real taste of the canyons and the treasures hidden within its walls, a few side trips off the pavement are required.

There are geodes here, but they are well-disguised. They are so similar in color and texture to the surrounding soil, the only way to locate one is to walk around breaking up dirt clods. The geodes are realtively common in some areas, but not all contain spectacular crystalizations.

Geodes found near Palo Duro Canyon are well-disguised.

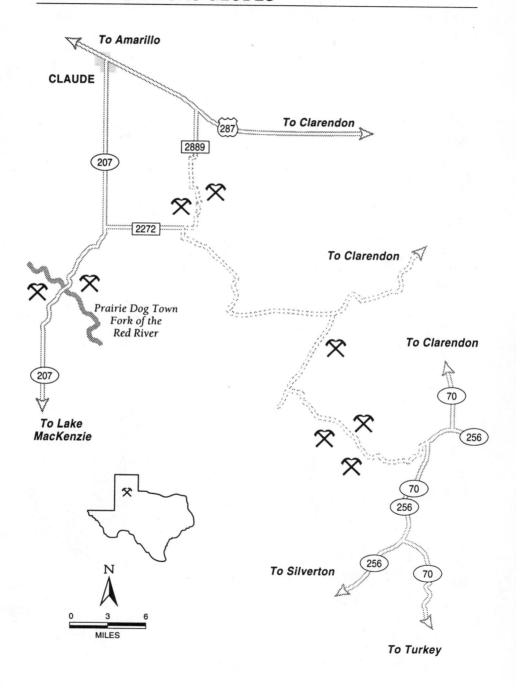

Not to be overlooked in the canyon is the cache of petrified woods and the occasional dinosaur bone. These and the geodes are most easily found in areas of erosion like creek beds. Other areas where past erosion has left beds of large cobbles are also good bets. These sites become obvious where dirt roads have been freshly graded.

Seasonal road conditions limit accessability to utility vehicles (though not necessarily four-wheel drives). The areas for collecting are deep within ranchland where fences are scarce. This doesn't mean however, that access to areas off the road is allowed without first seeking permission. Cattle and horses roam freely here, so proceed around any bend in the road with caution.

SITE 6 *SELENITE AND PETRIFIED WOOD AT LAKE MACKENZIE*

Land type: Canyon.
Elevation: 3,126 feet.
Best season: Fall.
Land manager: MacKenzie Municipal Water Authority.
Material: Petrified wood, selenite, barite roses.
Tools: None.
Vehicle: Any.
Accommodations: RV parking at the lake.

Selenite crystals sparkle in the sun from a hillside at MacKenzie Reservoir.

SITE 6   *SELENITE AND PETRIFIED WOOD AT LAKE MACKENZIE*

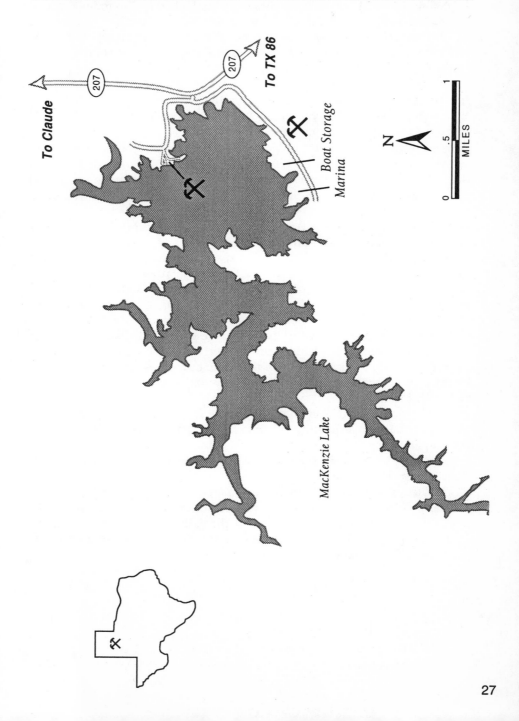

Special attractions: Caprock Canyons State Park, Palo Duro Canyon State Park.

Finding the site: From U.S. Highway 287 in Claude turn south on Texas Highway 207. The lake entrance is approximately forty-two miles south of town. The best collecting of all the materials is to the north of the lake. At the entrance gate turn right. Turn left at the first dirt road, bearing to the left at all road forks. Watch for the sparkle of the selenite at approximately 0.2 of a mile after turning off of the pavement.

Another good site for collecting the selenite is 0.8 of a mile to the left of the entrance gate, just past the dam. On the left side of the road are hills that appear to be almost pure gypsum, the glassy selenite crystals, some more than a foot in length, can be found throughout the mounds.

Alternate route: From U.S. Highway 87 in Tulia turn east on Texas Highway 86. Travel east for twenty-two miles. Turn north on Texas Highway 207. The lake entrance is about seven miles north of the turn.

Rockhounding: Millions of fragile selenite crystals glisten in the sunlight from the hillsides of Tule Canyon, surrounding MacKenzie Reservoir. But in your scramble to gather the best specimens don't overlook the chunks of petrified wood that also litter these hills. In places, the wood is so plentiful that the locations of entire fallen trees (shattered into thousands of pieces) are easily discernible. Much of the wood is nicely agatized, but even that which has less silica content, is so well preserved as to make quite interesting pieces. Distinct bark ridges are obvious, as are internal plant structures like xylem and phloem tubes.

Because barite occurs naturally with large gypsum deposits (selenite is a transparent form of gypsum), prized desert roses composed of barite are also found here. Look for them in the same outcroppings with the selenite crystals. Though most will be small, any size is possible in this mineral-rich environment.

The formations found in Tule Canyon are from the Pleistocene and Triassic eras. Both post-date the Permian rocks seen usually throughout the region. The canyon is the best site in the area for viewing geology from these eras and fossilized teeth and bones from several Triassic creatures can be found in the canyon.

The lake is part of the MacKenzie Municipal water district, which serves several nearby towns. Collecting is allowed on all water district property, with the purchase of an entry permit at the gate. Some of the land on the north shore is privately owned, however. Care should be taken not to trespass onto clearly marked private property.

SITE 7 *GRAVELS NEAR QUITAQUE*

Land type: Rolling plains.

Elevation: 2,570 feet.

Best season: Fall.

Land manager: Texas Department of Transportation.

Material: Agate, petrified wood, flint, fossils.

Tools: None.

Vehicle: Any.

Accommodations: Motel or bed-and-breakfast within 20 miles.

Special attractions: Caprock Canyons State Park, Palo Duro Canyon State Park.

Finding the site: Quitaque is on Texas Highway 86 between Turkey and Silverton. In Quitaque turn south on Farm Road 1065. Approximately ten miles from town, the road dead-ends into Texas Highway 97. Turn east. Gravel-bearing road cuts begin one mile after the turn and continue for more than two miles.

Rockhounding: More Ogalala gravel beds are located south of the town of Quitaque. Material similar to that found on Texas Highway 70 near Clarendon and Alanreed can be expected here, with the addition of small

Roadside collecting in the Ogalala gravel beds offer interesting possibilities.

SITE 7   *GRAVELS NEAR QUITAQUE*

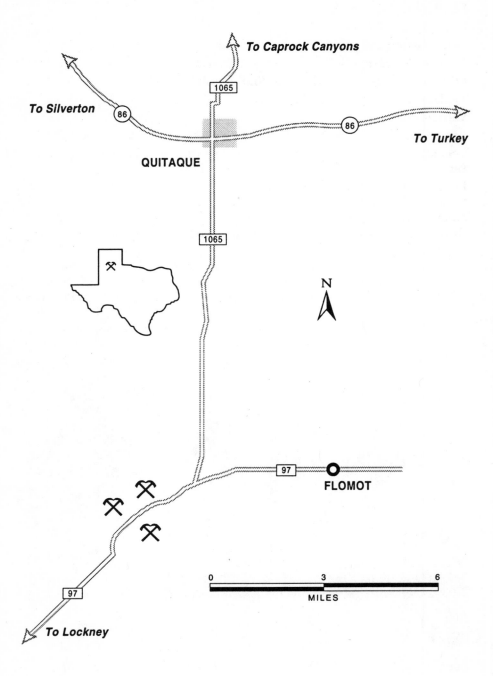

To Caprock Canyons

1065

To Silverton

86

To Turkey

86

QUITAQUE

1065

N

FLOMOT

97

97

To Lockney

0   3   6
MILES

white and tan fortification agates.

The agate is in small broken pieces, with a few larger pieces mixed in. There also seems to be an increased number of fossilized shells here. These are of unknown period, and are often tightly encased in the matrix material, but good specimens are possible with diligence. There are a few pieces of Alibates flint in the mixture but in smaller quantities than found to the north. These changes in content hold true as exposed gravel beds are sampled farther to the south as well.

SITE 8 *TURKEY ALABASTER*

Land type: Rolling plains, river breaks, canyons.

Elevation: 2,300 feet.

Best season: Fall.

Land manager: Texas Department of Transportation.

Material: Selenite, alabaster.

Tools: Hammers, chisels.

Vehicle: Any.

Accommodations: Hotel Turkey.

Special attractions: Hotel Turkey, Caprock Canyons State Park, Palo Duro Canyon State Park.

Finding the site: Turkey is located on Texas Highway 86, thirty miles west of Estelline (on U.S. Highway 287), or fifty-four miles east of Tulia (on Interstate Highway 27). In Turkey, turn north on Texas Highway 70/86. When the two highways split bear right to remain on Texas Highway 70. Alabaster can be collected along the road beginning just north of town and continuing for several miles.

Rockhounding: Boulders of alabaster with rose and gray variegations are scattered along the roadside north of Turkey. If you're interested in small chunks for carving, take chisels and hammers; if you're interested in anything larger, take strong help.

The soft material carves quite well by hand, and even beginners with a little creativity can fashion interesting pieces with little difficulty.

The town of Turkey is the home of country music singer Bob Wills, and a festival held in his honor swells the town to several thousand visitors every fall. Whether you plan on spending the night in town or not stop by the Hotel Turkey.

This restored hotel is operated as a bed-and-breakfast. Tell the owners, Scott and Jane Johnson, you're a rockhound, and they'll be happy to show you their collection out back. They have hauled in huge alabaster boulders from the surrounding area to decorate their pond and garden area. Some of the prettiest are in the pond itself, but be careful what you say, or Jane will be wading knee-deep in the water and proudly dragging them out for your inspection.

Boulders of alabaster line the roadside north of Turkey.

SITE 8 *TURKEY ALABASTER*

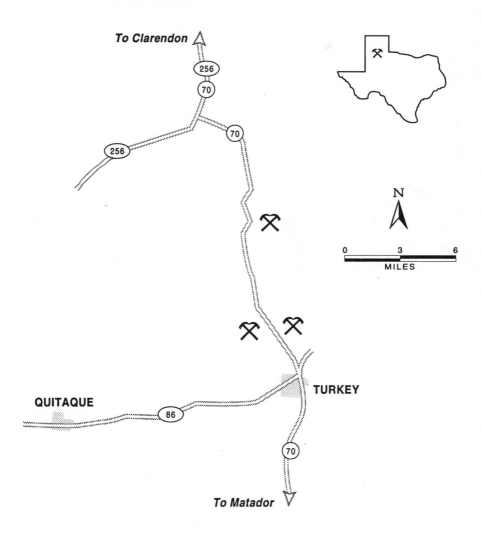

SITE 9 *FOSSILS NEAR RALLS*

Land type: Rolling plains.

Elevation: 3,108 feet.

Best season: Late summer or early fall.

Land manager: Texas Department of Transportation.

Material: Fossils, flint, agatized wood.

Tools: None.

Vehicle: Any.

Accommodations: Motels within 20 miles.

Special attraction: Ralls Historical Museum.

Finding the site: Ralls is located at the junction of Texas Highway 207 and U.S. Highway 62/82, approximately twenty-seven miles east of Lubbock. In Ralls, take Texas 207 south for thirteen miles. This brings you to the edge of the high plains escarpment known as the "Caprock." Collecting is good along the roadside immediately before and after the change in elevation.

Rockhounding: An unusual mixture of flint, agate and fossils can be found littering the roadsides south of the tiny farming town of Ralls. Most of the pebbles, which include flint, white banded agate, and agatized wood, are from the southern edge of the Ogalala gravels. These have mixed with fossils from nearby Lower Cretaceous and Permian formations. Small to medium species of clams seem to be the bulk of the lot, but many are nicely preserved with little matrix material attached.

Because the land surrounding the Caprock is heavily farmed, roadsides are frequently plowed when adjacent fields are planted. This can help or hinder good rock collecting. Large concentrations of stones can simply disappear until soaking rains once again compact the soil and bring the rocks to the surface. On the other hand, unusual finds are often possible in the freshly turned soil that might have otherwise been missed.

Most of the land is planted in cotton, so soils will be most compacted in late summer prior to harvest, and freshly turned in late fall or early winter. Even where there are no fences, be sure to ask permission before venturing beyond the roadside.

SITE 9   *FOSSILS NEAR RALLS*

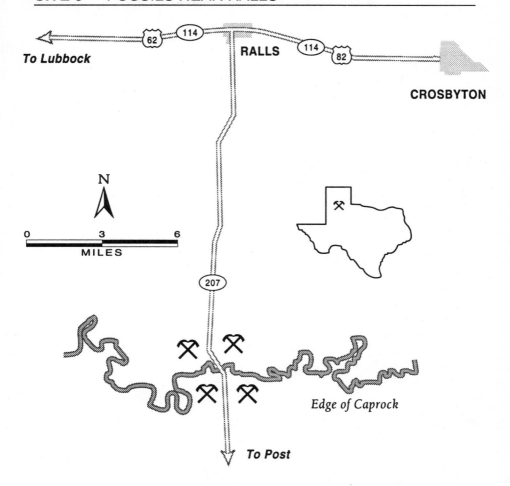

WEST TEXAS

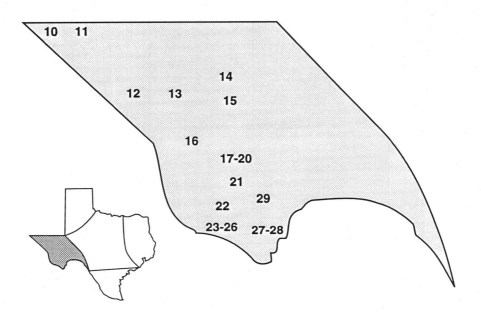

OVERVIEW

The violent geological history of West Texas makes this region one of the richest in the state's treasure trove. There are garnets in El Paso, opals in the region north of Big Bend, and the most beautiful agates the state has to offer are found throughout the region. Upper and Lower Cretaceous fossils are abundant. Isolated finds of chrysoprase, celestite, chrysocolla, and spectacular quartz crystals are the norm here. Petrified woods, including palm wood can be found in various areas, as can geodes. Cinnabar, silver, galena, hematite, and limonite are among the cache of minerals to be found here.

Roadside collecting is often quite productive. Because much of West Texas is mountainous, road cuts provide exposure of materials not otherwise found at the surface. There are several ranches in the Big Bend area open to collecting, and the ranchers in that area are quite amenable toward rockhounds. But be sure and ask permission to rockhound on private property.

Winter is the season of choice in the Big Bend area. Anytime from February through October, temperatures can become unbearable. In other areas of West Texas, collecting during late Fall is also quite comfortable.

Mule deer are hunted in West Texas between late November and mid-December. Care should be taken to avoid areas off of main roads during these times.

SITE 10 *GARNET IN THE FRANKLIN MOUNTAINS*

Land type: Mountains.
Elevation: 4,200 feet.
Best seasons: Fall, winter.
Land manager: Texas Department of Transportation.
Material: Garnet, serpentine schist.
Tools: Chisels, shovels.
Vehicle: Any.
Accommodations: RV parking, motels, and hotels within 10 miles.
Special attraction: Hueco Tanks State Park.
Finding the site: In El Paso take U.S. Highway 54 north to Texas Loop 375 North, which is also known as the Trans Mountain Road. Turn east on the Loop. Immediately after beginning the ascent into the mountains, there is an area suitable for parking on the right side of the road. The area for collecting is not in the actual road cut facing the highway but in the exposed mountainside about fifty feet to the left, facing the parking area. Look for the green color of the serpentine that colors the entire mountainside.

Rockhounding: The Franklin Mountains near El Paso hold a cache of surprising treasure in the deserts of West Texas. Green- banded serpentine schist, studded with garnet makes the trip to the far western edge of the state worthwhile. Some of the garnets are gem quality. Size range is considerable. Most of the crystals are a deep brown grossular variety, but an occasional find of emerald green uvarovite is possible.

The Franklin Mountains are primarily Precambrian granite and metamorphic rock (like the serpentine). This is only one of a handful of sites in the state where rocks of this age can be seen at the surface. The schist found here was once mudstone that was heated and pressurized before being tilted skyward.

Chiseling pieces from the face of the mountain is possible but not necessary, since garnet-studded schist and large serpentinite specimens cover the ground near the base of the mountain. The rubble is deep enough however, that careful digging for the best pieces is a good idea.

While there are no fences restricting access to areas farther down the hillside away from the road, no access to any area off the immediate roadside is allowed. This is a Fort Bliss artillery range.

The dark circular masses in this piece of serpentinite are garnet crystals.

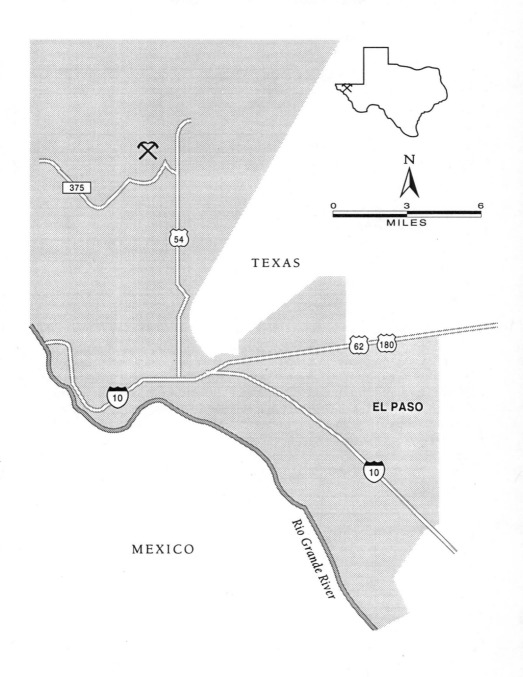

SITE 11 *AGATE AND FLINT NEAR HUECO TANKS*

Land type: Mountains.

Elevation: 3,700 feet.

Bext season: Winter.

Land manager: Texas Department of Transportation.

Material: Agate, flint.

Tools: Picks, gads, chisels.

Vehicle: Any.

Accommodations: RV parking and motels within 25 miles.

Special attraction: Hueco Tanks State Historical Site.

Finding the site: From El Paso take U.S. Highway 62/180 east. Mark mileage at the junction of Texas Highway 659 with U.S. 62/180. From that point, good road cut collecting begins approximately fifteen miles east and continues for four miles.

Rockhounding: Large specimens of gray flint combined with a few choice pieces of mottled burgundy agate make this site worth going out of the way for. Some of the flint is in pieces weighing more than twenty pounds, has good luster and some of it has interesting color mixtures.

The geology of the area between the Franklin Mountains in El Paso and the Hueco Mountains is quite interesting, and a trip to the Hueco Tanks State Historical Sight provides a look millions of years into the past. The "tanks" are depressions in limestone where water collects and pools. The hills containing the tanks are the remnant peaks of mountains that once towered over the Hueco Basin. Numerous Indian pictographs can be found through out the piles of boulders that surround the tanks, and guided tours are available to help you find the best.

After leaving the state park, heading west, many of the road cuts through the Hueco Mountains have exposed Magdalena limestone, which is rich in crinoid fossils, petrified wood, and chert/flint nodules.

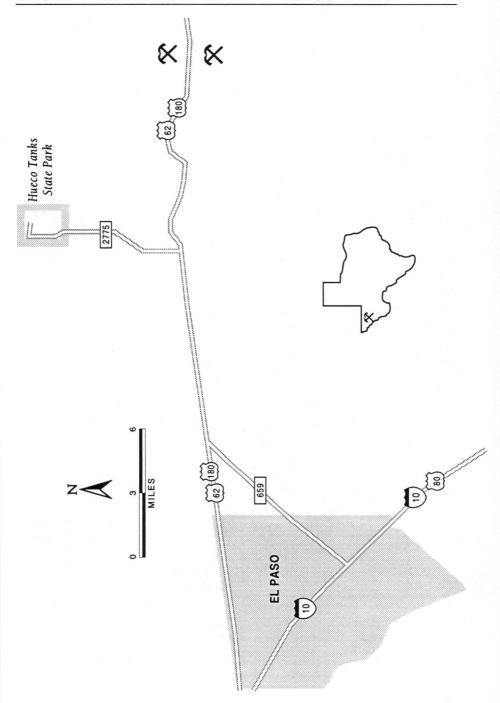

Pools of water collect among the limestone boulders at Hueco Tanks.

SITE 12 *ALLAMOORE TALC MINES*

Land type: Mountains.

Elevation: 4,010 feet.

Best season: Winter.

Land manager: Texas Department of Transportation.

Material: Talc.

Tools: Hammers, chisels.

Vehicle: Any.

Accommodations: RV parking and motels within 15 miles.

Special attraction: Guadelupe Mountains National Park.

Finding the site: Van Horn is approximately 121 miles east of El Paso on Interstate 10. Talc can be collected in road cuts on the Interstate, beginning five miles west of Van Horn, and continuing west for the next three miles. Chisels are a good idea, but finesse is required to extract nice-sized pieces of the fragile material.

Rockhounding: The mountains east and north of Van Horn hold a large cache of high quality talc. This deep gray green soft stone, also known as soapstone, is ideal for carving, and makes an interesting addition to any mineral collection.

With a hardness of only one on the Mohs scale, talc carves with an ease that few other minerals can surpass. It is one of the earliest materials used in artistic carving. Modern-day artists use a variety of tools on talc, including chisels, Dremel tools, and knives. Combined with other materials, talc carvings can make stunning sculptures, decorative boxes, and jewelry.

The talc is commercially mined by several companies near the ghost town of Allamoore. For a closer look at the mine operations, or to collect from the mine dumps, take exit 129 marked Allamoore/Hotwells from I-10. The mines and their processing plants are visible on the north side of the highway. After exiting the Interstate, take the first road to the north. It passes right through the processing plant. It would be advisable to check in at the office or call in advance, before any collecting is done. Call Dal Minerals at 915-283-9073.

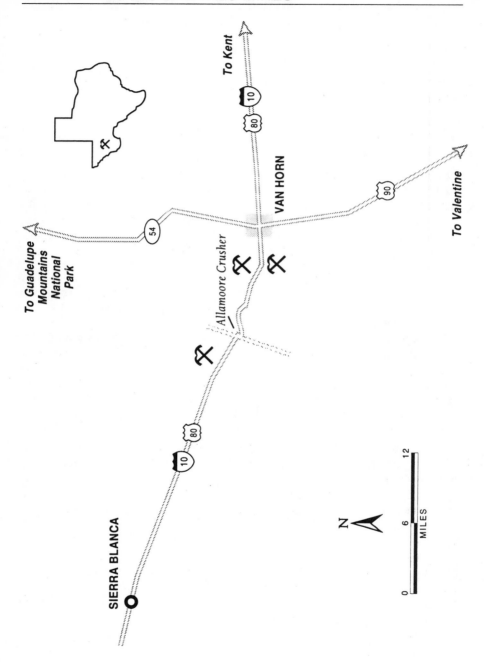

SITE 13 *KENT FOSSILS*

Land type: Mountains.

Elevation: 4,500 feet.

Best season: Winter.

Land manager: Texas Department of Transportation.

Material: Fossils, colored sandstone, agate, flint.

Tools: Hammer, chisels.

Vehicle: Any.

Accommodations: RV parking and motels within 40 miles.

Special attractions: McDonald Observatory, Fort Davis.

Finding the site: The site is located ten miles east of Kent where Interstate highways 10 and 20 converge. Look for the huge rubble piles between the two highways. The best access is from west-bound I-20 (there is a turn-around for east-bound traffic). Immediately before the two highways merge, there is a widened area suitable for parking. Be sure to park well off of the highway.

Rockhounding: There are more rocks here than one person could look at in a lifetime. That is the best description possible for this site. Some of the material found here appears to be rubble piled here when the highways were constructed. Because the area is rich in silica-based rock, the rubble is filled with petrified wood, agate, and flint. Also included are nice pieces of colored sandstone.

Beyond the rubble, is a stream bed known as Ninemile Draw, where layers of fossil-filled mudtone are exposed. Huge slabs of the rock can be loosened and removed. The fossils are Lower Cretaceous, with oysters and clams being the most abundant.

This is prime rattlesnake territory. If temperatures are above 70 degrees Fahrenheit, take all necessary precautions. Make lots of noise when approaching the site, and poke all weedy areas carefully with a stick before proceeding.

Time permitting, the drive through the nearby Davis Mountains is one of the most scenic the state has to offer. From Kent turn south on Texas Highway 118. It meets Texas Highway 17 just north of the town of Fort Davis, passing the McDonald Observatory along the way. If the observatory isn't of interest to you take Texas Highway 166 to the west when it meets TX 118 twenty-three miles south of Kent. It offers more spectacular mountain scenery and ends up just south of Fort Davis. As an added bonus, there is a quiet little RV park called Crow's Nest (no relation) on this road as you near Fort Davis.

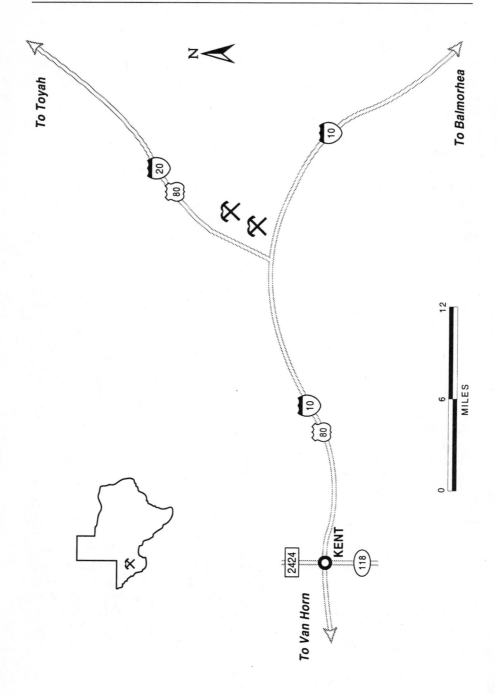

SITE 14 *TOYAH AGATE*

Land type: Desert plains.
Elevation: 2,580 feet.
Best season: Fall, winter.
Land manager: Texas Department of Transportation.
Material: Agate, petrified wood.
Tools: Shovel.
Vehicle: Any.
Accommodations: RV park with hookups, motels within 20 miles.
Special attractions: West of the Pecos Museum, Balmorhea State Park.

Finding the site: Toyah is located nineteen miles west of Pecos on Interstate 20. Roadside collecting on Ranch Road 2903 within a ten mile range south of Toyah is productive, but the best collecting seems to be on an unmarked county road heading west out of town. From Interstate 20 turn north into town. Cross the railroad tracks, turn right, then left on DuBois St. Remain on DuBois to Fourth Street. Turn left. This leads out of town. Good collecting possibilities abound along the road in any rocky area, for about seven miles.

Agates found near Toyah may contain small pockets of crystals.

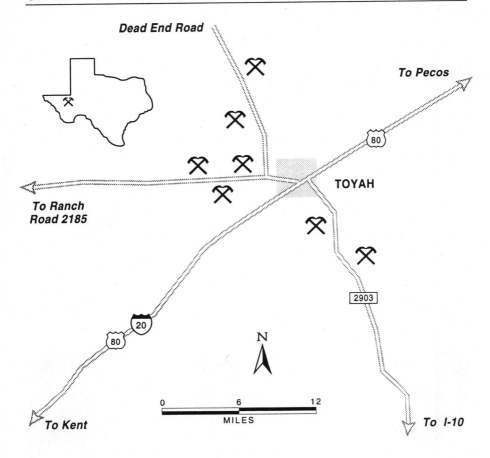

Rockhounding: Agate of every imaginable color can be found around this tiny town. The most prized pieces are those of a blue plume, which is so dark it appears black in the harsh West Texas sun.

Though the area is dotted with hills, it is a basin of sorts, filled with Quaternary sand and gravel washed in from higher ground. This basin is surrounded on three sides by distant agate-producing mountain ranges, hence the wide variety and large supply of the material. Small pieces of petrified wood are also available.

The town of Toyah itself, is a sleepy little place, with a few surprises. Once a bustling division point on the T&P Railway, many of the town's abandoned eighteenth century buildings still stand. One resident has spent several years building a mock Old West town on his property, where they hold an annual Mesquite Festival in July. Don't hesitate to stop for a quick look.

SITE 15 *BALMORHEA BLUE AGATE*

Land type: Lakeshore, hills.

Elevation: 3,205 feet.

Best season: Fall, winter

Land managers: Balmorhea Water District.

Material: Agate.

Tools: Picks, hammers.

Vehicle: Any.

Accommodation: RV camping and cabins at the state park.

Special attraction: Balmorhea State Park.

Finding the site: Balmorhea is approximately forty-seven miles west of Fort Stockton. It is located on Texas Highway 17 three miles southwest of Interstate 10. In town, signs point the way to the lake on Houston Street. There is a $2 fee for collecting, payable at the store on the right of the road as you approach the lake.

Rockhounding: The hills surrounding tiny Lake Balmorhea once were literally covered with chunks of deep blue agate commonly known as "Balmorhea Blue." Unfortunately the area is now quite picked over. Collec-

SITE 15 BALMORHEA BLUE AGATE

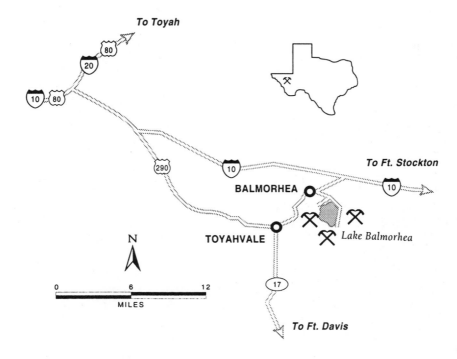

tors with patience, however, can still find a few good pieces. Most will be pebble sized or slightly larger and quite suitable for tumbling. The striking blue color, contrasted with white banding, makes this agate a popular item for jewelry-making.

Nearby Balmorhea State Park has some examples of the blue, as well as other rocks found in the area. The park is quite unusual, in that its focal point is a spring-fed swimming pool built in 1935 by the Civilian Conservation Corps. With 68,000 square feet of surface, it is one of the largest in the world and makes for a really cool dip on a hot West Texas day.

SITE 16 *MARFA AGATE*

Land type: Desert basin.

Elevation: 2,464 feet.

Best season: Winter.

Land manager: Texas Department of Transportation.

Material: Agate.

Tools: Hammers, picks.

Vehicle: Any.

Accommodations: Marfa.

Special attractions: Marfa Lights.

Finding the site: Marfa is located at the junction of U.S. highways 67 and 90 sixty-one miles north of the Mexican border. In town take U.S. 67 south. Beginning about nine miles south of town, good collecting is found in all road cuts and gravely areas. Other sites are located on Texas Highway 169, which intersects U.S. 67 seven miles south of Marfa.

Rockhounding: Many rockhounds will find it absolutely amazing that something as beautiful as bouquet agate can be found in such a desolate place as Marfa. The agate is abundant in small pieces, but fist-sized chunks of the multi-colored stone are not unusual.

Marfa lies near the edge of a huge basin, which is the remains of the Paisano Volcano that erupted about 35 million years ago. The area is surrounded by other mountains of volcanic origin and others that underwent tremendous metamorphic pressures. This makes the entire basin ideal for agate hunting.

Marfa itself has gained quite a reputation statewide for a reason other than beautiful rocks: the Marfa lights. This strange phenomenon, said to be similar to the Aurora Borealis, is as yet unexplained. Ask any local resident for the best place to view the spectacle.

Remember that the rattlesnakes far outnumber the people in Presidio County. Caution is advised in any rocky area, particularly rock ledges in the road cuts. Never put your feet or hands anywhere you can't see and poke suspect areas with a stick first.

SITE 16 *MARFA AGATE*

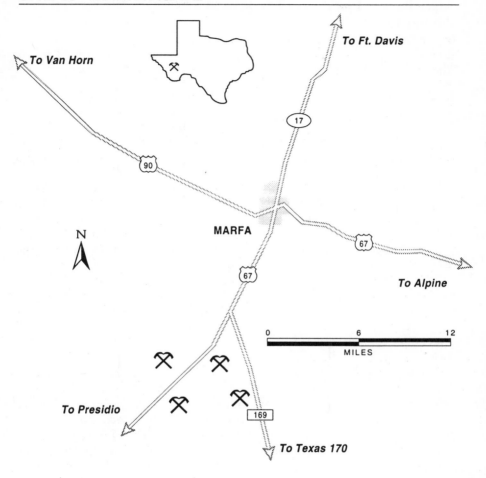

To Van Horn

To Ft. Davis

17

90

MARFA

67

67

To Alpine

N

0   6   12

MILES

To Presidio

169

To Texas 170

SITE 17 *WOODWARD RANCH RED PLUME*
AGATE AND OPALS

Land type: Desert mountains.
Elevation: 4,200 feet.
Best season: Winter.
Land manager: Woodward family, 915-364-2271.
Material: Red plume agate, opal.
Tools: Picks, chisels.
Vehicle: Any.

Accommodations: RV park nearby, motels in Alpine.

Special attraction: Big Bend National Park.

Finding the site: Woodward Ranch is located on Texas Highway 118 sixteen miles south of Alpine. The dirt road to the ranch is clearly marked on the west side of TX 118. Follow the dirt road 1.7 miles west from TX 118. The rock shop and headquarters is on the left side of the road.

Rockhounding: If there is one place in Texas where rockhounding heaven and hell meet it has to be at Woodward Ranch. It's heaven because it is rich with treasure and hounds are free to roam the ranch seeking it; it's hell because there are billions and billions of rocks to sort through to find the good stuff. And, unfortunately, the good stuff is often the same color and texture as the junk.

The four thousand acres on the ranch have been open to rockhounds for fifty years. People come from all over the world seeking the red plume agate, precious opal, carnelian, labradorite, and jasper, just to name a few. The Woodward family is on hand to give encouragement. They will show you the rough material, which is not always easy to distinguish from the red lava rock that covers the surface of the entire ranch.

The Woodward's own collection is quite extensive, and provides more than enough incentive to send you out into the hills in search of your own treasure. Though the ranch is quite well-known, and has been hunted for a half century, the availability of the agate has only slightly diminished. This is because every good rain erodes away the concealing topsoil and rock, exposing new finds.

The agate in this area formed in gas pockets in the lava flows from massive volcanic eruptions. Following the lava flows, the area was covered with volcanic ash nine hundred to one thousand feet thick. Silica-laden water seeped through the ash and into the pockets where it formed the agate. The beautiful colors come from mineral staining, which is why the agate is one color in one area, and yet another color twenty miles down the road.

Check in at the headquarters before beginning any hunting. The fee is currently fifty cents per pound for what you decide to keep.

In addition to the normal cautions about rattlesnakes, sturdy boots and long pants are highly recommended at this site to avoid injury from the many plant species with needles, thorns, and sharp edges that are indigenous to the area.

SITE 18 *MINERALS AT THE BIRD MINE*

Land type: Mountains.

Elevation: 3,800 feet.

Best season: Winter.

Land manager: Woodward family 915-364-2271.

Material: Galena, hematite, limonite.

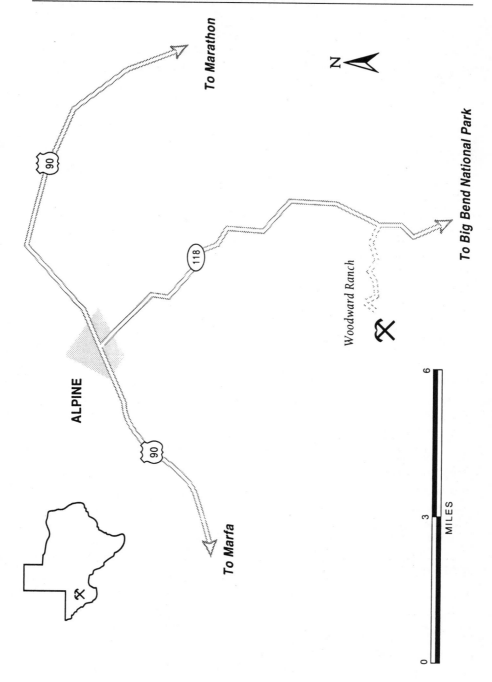

Tools: Shovel, hammer.

Vehicle: Any.

Accommodations: Motels and RV parking in Alpine.

Special attraction: Big Bend National Park.

Finding the site: Arrangements for hunting at the Bird Mine must be made at Woodward Ranch, which is located on Texas Highway 118, sixteen miles south of Alpine (see SITE 17). The dirt road to the ranch is clearly marked on the west side of TX 118. Follow the dirt road 1.7 miles to the ranch headquarters and rock shop.

Rockhounding: Mineral collectors will not want to pass up a trip to the remote Bird Mine located east of Alpine. Formerly a silver and lead operation, the dumps contain manganite, galena, hematite, and some very nice limonite cubes.

The mine is operated by the Woodward family of Woodward ranch south of Alpine. Advance arrangements must be made, and the charge is currently $15 per day with a 40-pound maximum. They prefer to take groups of four or five people. Call the ranch at 915-364-2271 for more information.

SITE 19   *POM POM AND GREEN MOSS AGATE AT NEEDLE PEAK*

Land type: Mountains.

Elevation: 2,720 feet.

Best season: Winter.

Land manager: Woodward family.

Material: Pom Pom and green moss agate.

Tools: Shovel and rock pick.

Vehicle: Utility.

Accommodations: Motels and RV campgrounds in Study Butte.

Special attraction: Big Bend National Park.

Finding the site: Though the actual collecting site is located near Big Bend National Park, advance arrangements must be made at Woodward Ranch. The ranch is located on Texas Highway 118 sixteen miles south of Alpine. The dirt road to the ranch is clearly marked on the west side of TX 118. Follow the dirt road 1.7 miles west from TX 118. The rock shop and headquarters is on the left side of the road.

Rockhounding: A slab of really good green moss agate should look like evergreen trees scattered across a snowy hillside. It should have clarity, depth, and vivid color. It is for agate of this quality that hounds from all over the world come to Needle Peak to collect.

Also found here is a wide range of pom pom agate. This agate has patterns that resemble clouds as a child might draw them, and half the fun of

SITE 19 POM POM AND GREEN MOSS AGATE AT NEEDLE PEAK
SITE 20 BREWSTER COUNTY AGATE AND CALCITE CRYSTALS

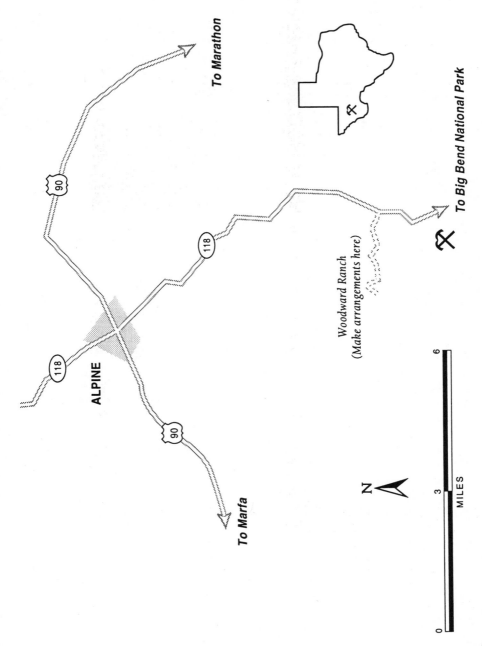

this agate is finding the shapes in the clouds. It isn't too difficult to find soaring gulls and majestic winged horses. These patterns allow for wonderful creativity for the jewelry maker.

Though the booty is good, this is a site that requires a good deal of work. There is some float material to be found, but the best pieces are found by digging. The site is off-road, and requires a moderate hike, making most collectors somewhat choosy about the pieces they pack out with them.

Excellent examples of all the material found at Needle Peak are on display at Woodward Ranch. The folks there will be happy to show you the rough stuff before you go, to make the search a little easier.

SITE 20 BREWSTER COUNTY AGATE AND CALCITE CRYSTALS

Land type: Desert mountains.
Elevation: 4,200 feet.
Best season: Winter.
Land manager: Texas Department of Transportation.
Material: Agate, calcite crystals.
Tools: Chisels.
Vehicle: Any.
Accommodations: Motels and RV parking within 25 miles.
Special attraction: Big Bend National Park.
Finding the site: From Alpine travel south on Texas Highway 118. The site is a road cut on the west side of the road about twenty-one miles south of Alpine. (Five miles south of the Woodward Ranch entrance.)

Rockhounding: The author was not the first to discover this road cut bearing veins of the red plume agate similar to that found at Woodward Ranch. The most prominent vein in the cut had been thoroughly worked by earlier visitors. Their leavings however, were enough to qualify this as a bonafide site.

Numerous small veins of agate peak through the tough volcanic rock throughout the road cut. Additionally, a portion of the cut contains very nice calcite and quartz crystals.

The hard part here will be extracting the material from the solid rock wall. Hammers, chisels, and gads are required, with safety goggles firmly in place. For those collectors who are less prepared or less willing to break a sweat, some very nice chips suitable for the tumbler should be available on the ground thanks to those who labored before.

This is an ideal site for rattlers. Anyone tenacious enough to think of climbing the face of the cut in search of treasure higher up should do so only on cool (65 degrees Fahrenheit or below) sunless days to avoid a face to face encounter with an angry sunbather.

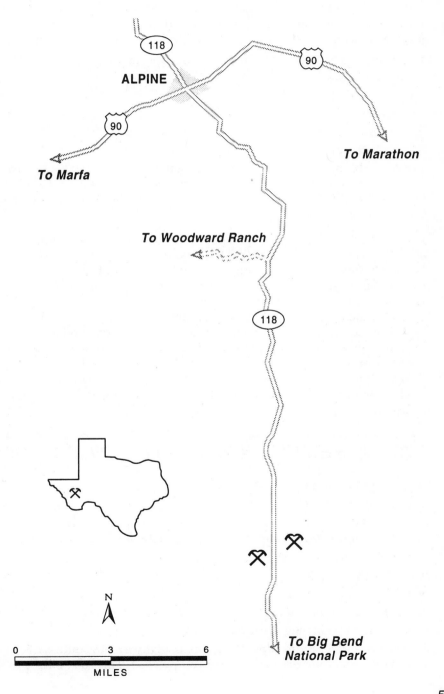

118

ALPINE

90

90

To Marathon

To Marfa

To Woodward Ranch

118

N

0   3   6

MILES

**To Big Bend
National Park**

SITE 21 *BREWSTER COUNTY AGATE AND WOOD*

Land type: Desert.
Elevation: 2,300 feet.
Best season: Winter.
Land manager: Texas Department of Transportation.
Material: Agate, petrified wood.
Tools: None.
Vehicle: Any.
Accommodations: Motels and RV parking within 40 miles.
Special attraction: Big Bend National Park.
Finding the site: From Alpine travel south on Texas Highway 118. At approximately forty miles south of Alpine, the terrain flattens. Good roadside collecting is found between the highway and the fence line throughout this basin.

Rockhounding: Flint, agate, and petrified wood samples are found strewn along the side of the road as TX 118 passes through a low lying basin of Lower Cretaceous rock surrounded by volcanic mountains.

The flint is gray and flecked with brown and red. The agate can be almost any color or variety found in the surrounding mountain ranges. (The author found a nice example of black plume.) The wood is in small pieces, though some are large enough for cabbing. As with most wood found in this area, it is well agatized, likely to be colorful, and should take a nice polish. Some palm wood reportedly has been found in the area as well.

Although the author found no fossils, the region is known for producing interesting specimens, including trilobites, graptolites, and some very unusual brachiopods.

SITE 22 *HEN EGG MOUNTAIN PETRIFIED WOOD*

Land type: Desert mountains.
Elevation: 5,005 feet.
Best season: Winter.
Land manager: Texas Department of Transportation.
Material: Petrified wood.
Tools: Shovels, pick.
Vehicle: Utility.
Accommodations: RV parking and motels in Study Butte.
Special attraction: Big Bend National Park.
Finding the site: From Alpine take Texas Highway 118 south 63.5 miles. Turn west on an unmarked, unpaved county road. This road passes to the

south of Hen Egg Mountain. Petrified wood is plentiful along the road for about five miles.

Rockhounding: Basketball-sized chunks of petrified wood are quite possible in the area near Hen Egg Mountain, but digging tools are necessary to pry larger pieces from the hard desert ground. Any brown rock protruding from the ground should be examined and excavated. Sharp-eyed hounds can easily haul hundreds of pounds of material away from this site.

The wood is well agatized, and takes a polish nicely, showing a fare amount of color. Small pieces of opalized wood can also be found here. As with any area in the region, don't overlook the possibility of agates.

This road meets up with Texas Highway 170 in Terlingua. Seasonal conditions may make the road difficult to traverse in low-lying areas. The land surrounding the road is private ranch property, and no collecting should be done beyond the roadside without first obtaining permission. This is especially true during deer hunting season.

SITE 22   *HEN EGG MOUNTAIN PETRIFIED WOOD*
SITE 23   *CINNABAR AT TERLINGUA MINES*
SITE 24   *AGATE, WOOD, AND FOSSILS NEAR TERLINGUA*

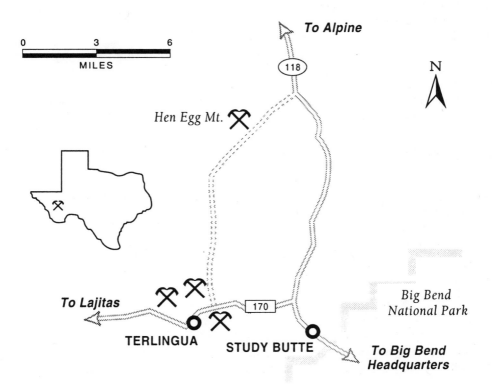

SITE 23 *CINNABAR AT TERLINGUA MINES*

Land type: Desert mountains.

Elevation: 2,720.

Best season: Winter.

Land manager: Terlingua Trading Company.

Material: Cinnabar, fossils.

Tools: Shovel.

Vehicle: Any.

Accommodations: Motels and RV parking within 10 miles.

Areas of interest: Ghost town ruins, river rafting excursions, chili cook-off in November.

Finding the site: The ghost town of Terlingua is located just north of Farm Road 170, approximately 4.5 miles west of Study Butte. Signs on FR 170 point the way up a dirt road to the ghost town. The Terlingua Trading Co. is at the top of the hill, past the cemetery.

Rockhounding: Brilliant red cinnabar specimens are available to collectors with some time and quite a lot of patience to search the mine dumps at Terlingua. Lower Cretaceous fossils are also found throughout the limestone tailings and in areas of erosion.

After the discovery of mercury ore, Terlingua became a thriving town of nearly two thousand people, almost entirely miners and their families. The mines here once produced almost one quarter of the nation's mercury. The mines operated from 1894 through the early 1970s, when demand diminished.

Cinnabar, or mercury sulfide, is a precipitate ore left in small cavities and fissures in the surrounding limestone beds and volcanic rocks. After the ore was brought to the surface, it was crushed and heated to release pure mercury vapor, which was then condensed to liquid form.

The dumps that seem most productive for collecting specimens are those directly in front of and downhill from the Trading Company. The dump nearest the Trading Company to the rear, is a fruitless effort. The miners apparently chased a small vein deep into the hillside without ever finding the mother lode.

None of the mines themselves are open to collecting. Be sure to check in at the Trading Company before you begin. They may be able to point you in the right direction, and also have some nice pieces for sale, just in case you have no luck on your own.

One other word of caution regarding this area: rockhounds often have the habit of tasting rocks in their efforts to identify the source material. Mercury is highly poisonous, and trace quantities would be both harmful and invisible to the naked eye, so tasting anything found here is downright dangerous.

That statement may or may not apply to the chili you would find here during the annual chili cook-off held in early November. You are on your own with that stuff. Proceed with caution.

SITE 24 *AGATE, WOOD, AND FOSSILS NEAR TERLINGUA*

Land type: Desert mountains.
Elevation: 2,720 feet.
Best season: Winter.
Land manager: Texas Department of Transportation.
Material: Agate, petrified wood, and fossils.
Tools: None.
Vehicle: Any.
Accommodations: Motels and RV parking within 10 miles.
Special attractions: Ghost town of Terlingua, river rafting excursions.
Finding the site: From the town of Terlingua (not the ghost town) take Farm Road 170 west about 2 miles. At that point, a dry tributary to Terlingua Creek crosses the road. Collecting is allowed in the creek bed, provided no fences are crossed.

Rockhounding: The laws of gravity apply here. Loose rocks move in a downward direction, especially when helped along with a little water. These facts make Terlingua Creek and its tributaries a prime spot for hounds in search of just about anything the Big Bend area has to offer.

Careful search of the river rocks can produce agate, petrified wood, cinnabar, quartz, fossils, and a beautiful rose-colored flint that the author found only in this creek bed. The agate is difficult to spot, mostly hidden behind rough weathered exteriors. When in doubt, take home any suspected rocks. Though not abundant, cinnabar specimens are as likely here as in the mine dumps themselves, since this site is directly downhill from several prominent tailing piles.

Even in midwinter the temperature here is likely to climb. A float trip down the Rio Grande River can be a cool diversion. Numerous excursion companies are found in Study Butte, Terlingua, and Lajitas. Trips vary in length from half-day to a full week, and there is no better way to see the stunning canyons that separate Texas and Mexico than from the river that created them.

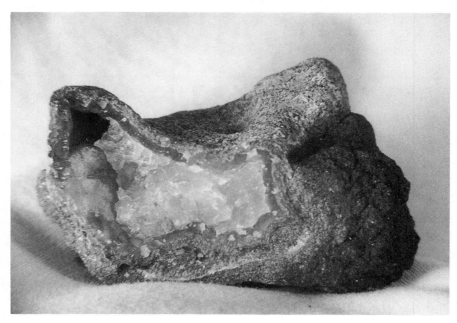

Not all of the nodules found at geode hill have complete cavities.

SITE 25 *GEODES NEAR LAJITAS*

Land type: Desert mountains.

Elevation: 2,200 feet.

Best season: Winter.

Land manager: Texas Department of Transportation.

Material: Geodes, agate nodules, quartz crystals.

Tools: Chisels.

Vehicle: Any.

Accommodations: Motel and RV parking in Lajitas.

Special attractions: Golf, rafting, horseback riding, scenic drive to Presidio.

Finding the site: Lajitas is located on Farm Road 170 between Terlingua and Presidio. From Lajitas go west on Farm Road 170 for two miles. The road cut bearing the geodes is on the north side of the road.

Rockhounding: This site is dubbed "geode hill." Though very small, the geodes found in this road cut are plentiful. They have an attractive green outside, and tiny crystals inside, surrounded by earthtone agate banding. The nodules which do not contain cavities are generally solid blue-gray agate inside.

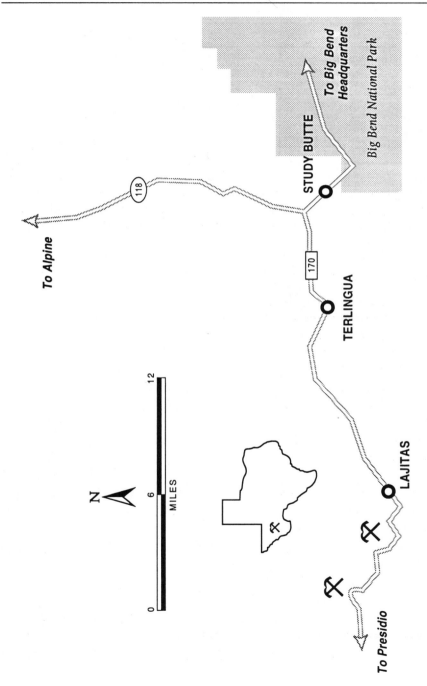

The road cut consists of layered lava and ash. The geodes and agate nodules are found in the green-tinted ash layer. They range from marble to fist size. Because the ash is relatively soft in places, many of the nodules have eroded out of the rock wall, littering the ground. Others must be carefully chipped from the ash. Even in areas where the ash is harder, this is not too difficult.

This is the type of road cut where it would be tempting to gather all the nodules you can find, but it is preferable to control your collecting desires so that others might share in the fun. It could be presumed that the embedded nodules continue into the mountainside indefinitely, but short of bringing down the entire mountain, eventually there will be a limit to the productivity of the cut.

It should not be a difficult chore to find other things to do in this area that will tempt you away from this fun site. Lajitas (formally known as Lajitas on the Rio Grande) is a commercial venture that lives up to its advertising. Besides the attractive hotel and RV park, the town offers horseback riding, river rafting, golf, and lots of hospitality. There are even a landing strip and hanger facilities for those who travel the country from the air.

Down at ground level, what is perhaps the most spectacular scenic drive in the state is found along Farm Road 170 between Lajitas and Presidio. The road winds along through volcanic mountains, following the Rio Grande River. The awesome forces of nature become quite apparent along the drive, as you pass through areas where massive volcanic boulders cover entire valleys. In other areas, the road rises to present spectacular views of the river. It is a drive well worth finding time for. If you can't make the entire one-hundred-mile round trip, at least drive ten or fifteen miles west from Lajitas for a small sample.

SITE 26 *CELESTITE NEAR LAJITAS*

Land type: Desert mountains.

Elevation: 2,200.

Best season: Winter.

Land manager: Texas Department of Transportation.

Material: Celestite, quartz.

Tools: Picks, hammers, chisels.

Vehicle: Any.

Accommodations: Motels and RV parking in Lajitas.

Special attraction: Lajitas to Presidio scenic drive.

Finding the site: Lajitas is located on Farm Road 170 between Terlingua and Presidio. From Lajitas go west on Farm Road 170 for four miles. The celestite is found in the road cut on both sides of the road.

Rockhounding: In Big Bend country, there is one word that describes the

Selenite crystals are plentiful on the ground near Persimmon Gap.

variety of rocks available: diverse. You don't like what you find in one area, simply move a short distance to find something entirely different. This road cut is a good example of that. The material here is not found in any other cuts along Farm Road 170.

The celestite and quartz crystals are small, but intriguingly set in colorful rocks bearing deposits of sulfur, green ash, and a sky-blue fuzzy material that even the author's favorite geologist could not readily identify. With some persistence, nice specimens suitable for rough display can be obtained.(And the blue stuff is a sure-fire conversation starter.)

SITE 27 *PERSIMMON GAP AGATE AND SELENITE*

Land type: Desert.
Elevation: 2,300 feet.
Best season: Winter.
Land manager: Texas Department of Transportation.
Material: Selenite, desert roses, flint, agate.
Tools: Camera.
Vehicle: Any.
Accommodations: RV parking at Stillwell; Gage Hotel in Marathon.
Special attractions: Stillwell Ranch, Big Bend National Park.

SITE 27 *PERSIMMON GAP AGATE AND SELENITE*
SITE 28 *STILLWELL RANCH AGATE AND WOOD*

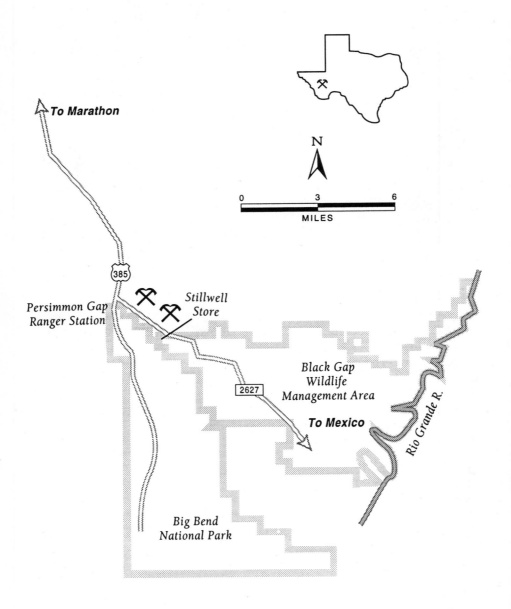

To Marathon

N

| 0 | 3 | 6 |

MILES

385

Persimmon Gap
Ranger Station

*Stillwell
Store*

*Black Gap
Wildlife
Management Area*

2627

To Mexico

Rio Grande R.

*Big Bend
National Park*

Finding the site: Persimmon gap is the name given to the northernmost ranger station in Big Bend National Park. It is located just inside the park boundary on U.S. Highway 385. From Persimmon Gap take U.S. 385 north about two miles to Ranch Road 2627. Turn right. The road cut is on the north side of the road, about five miles after turning. It is at the top of the highest hill on this road.

Rockhounding: A waterfall of crystals cascades down the face of this road cut. The wonders seem endless as each new outcropping presents a different variety. From delicate selenite bunches to jagged calcite teeth. Barite roses blend casually with the glittering crystals. There are also some nice-sized white flint and agate nodules embedded in the cut near the ground, some containing quartz crystal banding.

This is a site that the author was hesitant to include in this book. It is a shining example of nature's beauty, and the destruction of it by over-eager collectors is not the desire of the author. The most prudent among us will simply take pictures and a few loose pieces found on the ground, without ever laying a hand upon the treasure.

Fortunately, nature has its own staff of security guards. This place has more snake holes than any the author encountered statewide. Do not even attempt to look at this site if the temperature is above sixty-five degrees Fahrenheit. Just roll down your car window, take a quick look through your binoculars or telephoto lens, then move on to the agate, crystals, and petrified wood awaiting down the road at Stillwell Ranch.

SITE 28 *STILLWELL RANCH AGATE AND WOOD*

Land type: Desert hills.

Elevation: 2,300 feet.

Best season: Winter.

Land manager: Stillwell family.

Material: Agate, petrified wood, quartz crystals, picture rock.

Tools: Hammer, chisels, pry bars, rock pick.

Vehicle: Utility.

Accommodations: RV parking at Stillwell, Gage Hotel in Marathon.

Special attraction: Black Gap Wildlife Management Area.

Finding the site: The Stillwell Ranch is located on Ranch Road 2627 east of Big Bend National Park. From the park take U.S. Highway 385 north to Persimmon Gap Ranger station. From the ranger station travel two miles north on U.S. 385 to Ranch Road 2627. Turn east. The town of Stillwell is located just over six miles southeast on this road. At the store inquire about collecting. From Marathon, Ranch Road 2627 is thirty-nine miles south on U.S. 385.

Rockhounding: As with Woodward Ranch near Alpine, the Stillwell family operates a working cattle ranch, but cater to rockhounds seeking the treasures of the Big Bend area as well. Besides numerous varieties of agate and jasper, the ranch is home to large deposits of petrified wood, including some palm wood. Also to be found here is a wide variety of crystals, and some colorful picture rock.

The Stillwell Store offers RV sites with hookups and shade (a very important commodity in this area). The fee for collecting is currently fifty cents per pound. The store has a nice display of the material found on the ranch, and they will be happy to point you in the right direction to get you started.

For more information or group planning, contact the Stillwells at 915-376-2244 or HC 65, Box 430, Alpine, Texas 79830.

SITE 29 *CHRYSOPRASE NEAR MARATHON*

Land type: High desert.
Elevation: 4,043 feet.
Best season: Winter.
Land manager: Texas Department of Transportation.
Material: Chrysoprase, flint, jasper.
Tools: None.
Vehicle: Any.
Accommodations: Gage Hotel in Marathon.
Area of interest: Gage Hotel.
Finding the site: Marathon is located near the junction of U.S. highways 90 and 385, forty miles north of Big Bend National Park. From Marathon take U.S. 385 south ten miles to a roadside picnic area. Collecting is along the road on both sides.

Rockhounding: A dazzling array of multi-colored flint and jasper, some of it apple green chrysoprase, covers the roadside south of Marathon. While much of the material is small, pieces large enough for cabbing are possible. The green material comes in a wide range of shadings and qualities, but careful hounds can find gem quality stones among the mixture. The jasper here is blazing red and orange. The flint ranges from banded black and gray to a mottled pink.

The picnic area here has what is know as a "walkover," or ladder over the fence. While some folks might interpret this as an open invitation to the land on the other side, quite often walkovers are placed by oil companies who need to check equipment or pipelines on the property. Therefore, it is still advisable to seek permission before crossing any fences onto private property.

When you have searched to your heart's content for that perfect piece

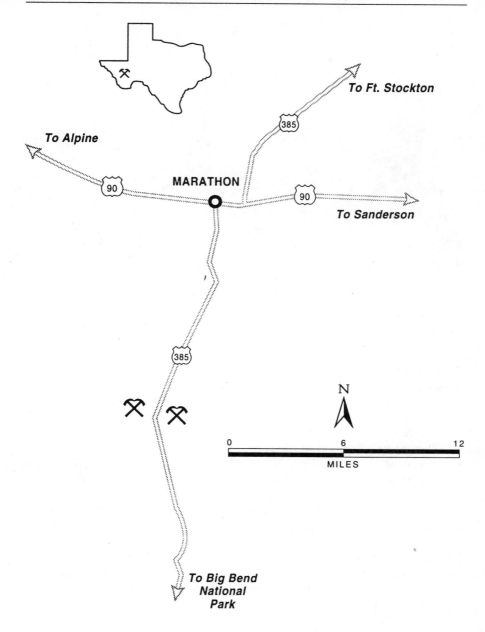

To Ft. Stockton

385

To Alpine

90

MARATHON

90

To Sanderson

385

N

| 0 | 6 | 12 |

MILES

To Big Bend
National
Park

The road from Marathon is long and dry.

of prase, mosey into town and take a step back in time at the Gage Hotel. The Gage isn't just an old hotel that somebody restored to make a buck. When J.P. and Mary Jon Byran of Houston purchased the hotel, they set out to create a masterpiece of craftsmanship and artistry that showcases the rugged beauty of the southwest. What they accomplished cannot be rivaled anywhere in Texas.

When they tell you that the rooms in the old part of the hotel have no private baths, don't shy away. Venture down the hall to see the splendor of the Mexican-tiled showers, and the coziness of the antique-filled rooms before you decide.

But if you insist on privacy, the historical beauty of the old hotel is now mirrored by twenty additional rooms (with baths). They are complete with Mexican fireplaces and surround a peaceful courtyard. The two sections are joined together by another courtyard and a stunningly beautiful swimming pool. All the rooms, old and new, stay filled most of the year, so don't expect to just drop in for the night. Reservations can be made by calling 915-386-4205.

CENTRAL TEXAS

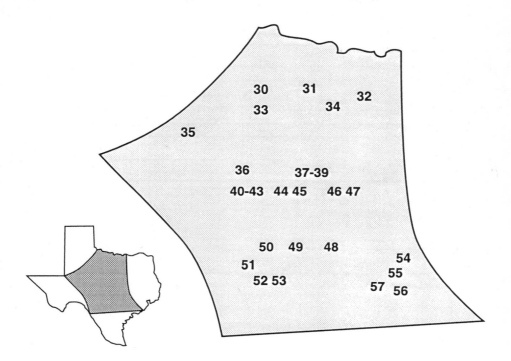

OVERVIEW

Texas' chief gemstone collecting areas are found in the central portion of the state. Topaz is found in Mason County, as are smoky and rose quartz. Collecting sites for fossils from Upper and Lower Cretaceous and Pennsylvanian eras ring the Hill Country of Central Texas. Look for Precambrian granite in various colors in the very heart of the region. Don't overlook caches of flint and agate in gray, blue-gray, and chocolate brown tucked away in the hillsides and stream beds throughout the area.

As in other areas of the state, roadside collecting offers a fair amount of opportunity. Numerous streams and rivers crisscross the region, and the banks of any navigable river are fair game to collectors, as is any lake shore not on privately owned land, or encompassed by a state park. In Mason county, there are two ranches that publicly seek rockhounds in search of topaz.

71

Late summer presents the safest collecting opportunities here. Temperatures generally remain in the nineties, with a few days being more moderate. Spring presents an unusual problem with a profusion of wildflower blooms. They not only hide rockhound treasure along the roadside, they attract massive quantities of bees.

Fall and Winter are almost entirely off limits for collecting in this part of the state due to the huge influx of deer hunters. The season runs from November to January. Some collecting might be possible in February, although javelina are hunted then in some areas. An October archery season on deer may also pose a problem for fall collectors. It is advisable to check with the Texas Parks and Wildlife Department for detailed information. They publish an annual guide listing seasons by county. Write TPWD, 4200 Smith School Rd., Austin, Texas 78744, or call 1-800-792-1112. The guide should also be available at retail stores that carry hunting supplies.

SITE 30 *HEMATITE AT HUBBARD CREEK RESERVOIR*

Land type: Plains.

Elevation: 1,220 feet.

Best season: Late summer.

Land manager: Hubbard Creek Water District.

Material: Hematite pebbles.

Tools: None.

Vehicle: Any.

Accommodations: Motels within 20 miles.

Special attraction: Fishing.

Finding the site: Hubbard Creek Reservoir is located near the junction of U.S. highways 180 and 183. The town of Breckenridge is east of the lake. From Breckenridge take Farm Road 3099 north 3.6 miles. The road will cross two sections of the dam, then fork to the right as Water District Road 277. Take the water district road 1.5 miles to a road cut directly behind the main dam. Collecting is on the right side of the road.

Rockhounding: An unusually large quantity of hematite pebbles in varying sizes is found in this hidden spot near Hubbard Creek Reservoir. For those unfamiliar with the field characteristics of hematite, look for globular-shaped pebbles and cobbles. They will be dark brown to gray, many almost black. They will feel very heavy in the hand, due to a relatively high specific gravity of 4.9 to 5.3. When using a streak plate, they will show a deep brown to reddish streak.

The pebbles here are quite suitable for cutting and polishing; it's not difficult to find pieces large enough for cabbing. The smaller pieces also

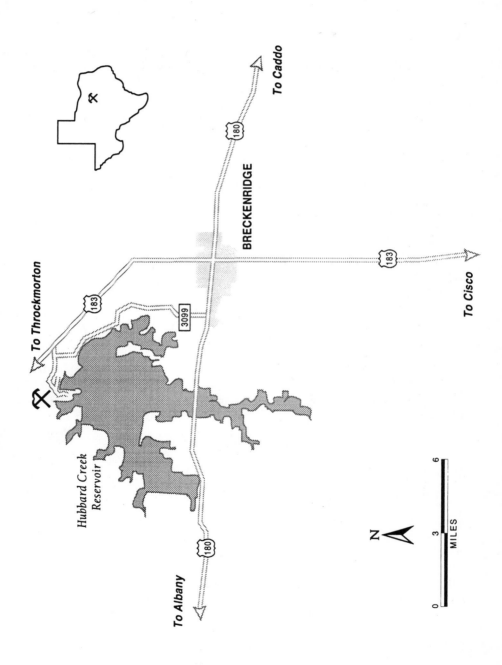

tumble nicely. Keep in mind though, that they will turn the slurry quite red. Any light-colored material that is semi-porous is best left for another batch, in order to prevent staining.

Consisting of iron oxide, hematite occurs throughout the United States. It can be present in formations of sedimentary, igneous, or metamorphic origin, making the presence of the pebbles here not highly unusual. Samples have also been collected at other lakes in the area.

Hubbard Creek Reservoir covers 15,250 acres, with more than one hundred miles of shoreline. The fishing is good, and the scenery superb. Wildlife in the area is quite varied. The author had a chance encounter with a bobcat near the collecting site. But don't let this keep you away, these small wildcats are just about as afraid of people as we are of them.

SITE 31 *MINERAL WELLS FOSSILS*

Land type: Rolling hills.

Elevation: 134 feet.

Best season: Late Summer.

Land manager: Texas Department of Transportation.

Material: Fossils, jasper, agate.

Tools: Pick.

Vehicle: Any.

Accommodations: RV parking and motels within 5 miles.

Special attractions: Hot wells in South Bend.

Finding the site: Mineral Wells is located approximately forty-six miles west of Ft. Worth on U.S. Highway 180. From Mineral wells take U.S. 180 east. At approximately 4.8 miles from the city limit, look for a rocky road cut on both sides of the road.

Rockhounding: Fossils from Upper and Lower Cretaceous periods, as well as the Pennsylvanian era are possible at this site. Root castings are plentiful, as are small specimens of petrified wood. Jasper in various colors, including pale green is also easily found here. Perhaps the most interesting treasure to be found at this site are conglomerate rocks with clear agate veins crisscrossing the interior.

The agate is not in large deposits, but these rocks are real eye-catchers when cut. Look for white or gray granular rocks about the size of a woman's fist. It is also possible to find smooth versions of these rocks, which appear to have been weathered and river polished. This polishing often reveals the agate veins.

The author was told that the rocks can also be found to the north of Mineral Wells, near the town of Perin, but I had no luck. An example of the agate-bearing rock, and others found in the area can be seen at a nameless rock and junktique shop on the north side of U.S. 180, just east of Mineral

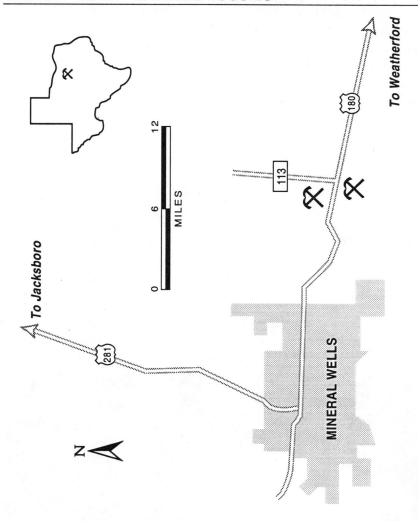

Wells. Perhaps the owner will point you in the right direction for finding the agates; if not, you'll at least enjoy seeing his collection.

After a long day of collecting, the mineral baths near South Bend are a sure cure for stiff joints. In fact, many people claim the waters are capable of curing quite a few things. The bath house is open from 9 a.m. to 6 p.m. Monday through Saturday and 1 p.m. to 5 p.m. on Sunday. To get there from Mineral Wells take Texas Highway 337/16 about thirty-three miles northwest to Graham. In Graham take Texas Highway 67 south approximately ten miles to South Bend. In South Bend turn west on Farm Road 701. The baths are located about two miles west of town. For further information, call 817-362-4423.

SITE 32 *WEATHERFORD FOSSILS*

Land type: Rolling hills.

Elevation: 1,052 feet.

Best season: Late summer.

Land manager: Texas Department of Transportation.

Material: Fossils.

Tools: None.

Vehicle: Any.

Accommodations: RV parking and motels in Mineral Wells.

Special attraction: Fort Worth Museum of Science and History.

Finding the site: Weatherford is located just off of Interstate 20, about twenty-five miles west of Fort Worth. In Weatherford take Texas Highway 171 south for two miles. Turn left at Farm Road 51. Any areas of surface exposure present good collecting. At the time of publication, good sites were at 5.3 and 6 miles from the turn to FR 51.

Rockhounding: Some of the nicest specimens of individual Turritella snails to be found in the state can be found in the region between Weatherford and Granbury. Several species are possible. The shells are found embedded in the limestone here as well. Also in this area are numerous oysters and some intriguing castings, some of them several inches in diameter and often bearing the snail shells.

The area around Weatherford is excellent for collecting fossils.

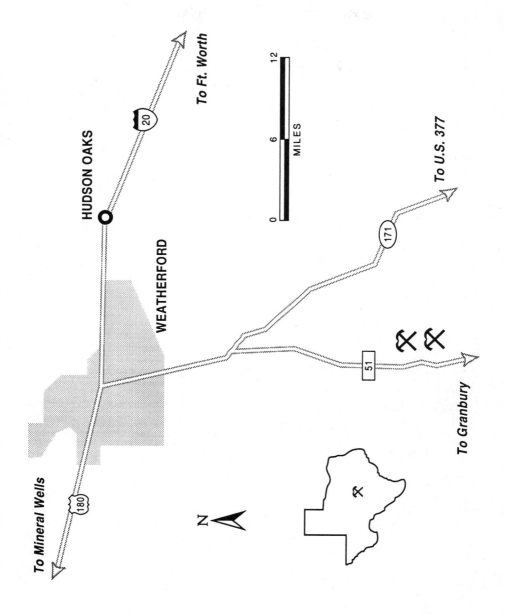

Both Upper and Lower Cretaceous fossils are possible here, but Lower Cretaceous seem to be the most prevalent. The fossils are abundant throughout the area, and the only trick to finding them is finding a site free of vegetation, where the rocks are exposed at the surface. Best bets are areas of erosion, like drainage ditches, or rocky hillsides.

In nearby Fort Worth, the Museum of Science and History has a wide range of exhibits, including fossils and local minerals. The exhibits are quite extensive; plan to spend an afternoon. The museum is located at 1501 Montgomery St., on Amon Carter Square. It is closed on Monday.

Fort Worth is quite underrated as far as Texas' tourist towns go. It has a wealth of attractions that will suit the tastes of almost any traveler, including one of the most outstanding zoos in the state, two western art museums, shopping, cultural events, and a downtown area painted with stunningly beautiful murals.

SITE 33 *CISCO FOSSILS*

Land type: Rolling plains.

Elevation: 1,608 feet.

Best season: Late summer.

Land manager: Texas Department Of Transportation.

Material: Fossils.

Tools: Picks, chisels.

Vehicle: Any.

Accommodations: Motels within 20 miles.

Special attraction: Fishing.

Finding the site: Cisco is located about one hundred miles west of Fort Worth on Interstate Highway 20. From Cisco take Texas Highway 6 north for about ten miles. Look for areas of erosion, such as drainage ditches or rocky hillsides.

Rockhounding: Cisco is a widely known fossil collecting area. This is due to both the availability and the wide range of specimens found. Fossils from the Lower Cretaceous period are found in addition to the abundant Pennsylvanian era specimens. The list of things to look for here is vast, including crinoid stems and heads, brachiopods, trilobites, and echinoids.

Once again, the trick here is to find a workable site that is relatively free of vegetation. Sites where natural rock outcrops exist are likely to be the most productive. Think small to hit it big here. This is not a site where the fossils jump off the ground and beg to be taken home as in some other locales. They are not only tiny but well mixed with other materials like sand and gravel. What can often appear to be nothing more than a pile of rocks can often produce handfuls of worthy specimens to the sharp-eyed collector.

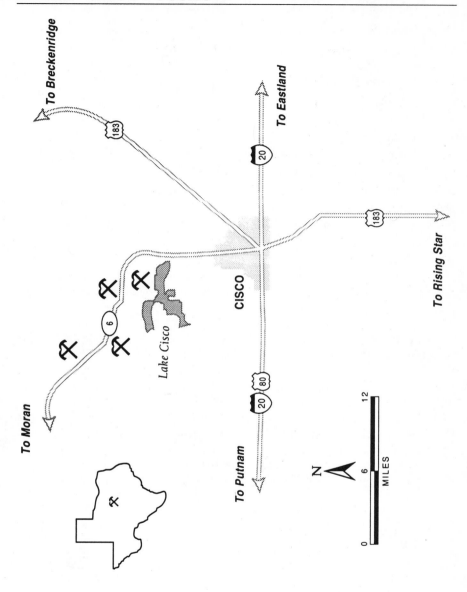

SITE 34 *GRANBURY FOSSILS*

Land type: Rolling hills.

Elevations: 725 feet.

Best season: Late summer.

Land manager: Texas Department of Transportation.

Material: Fossils.

Tools: Pick.

Vehicle: Any.

Accommodations: RV parking and motel in Granbury.

Special attraction: Dinosaur Valley State Park.

Finding the site: Granbury is located forty-one miles southwest of Fort Worth on U.S. Highway 377. In Granbury take Texas Highway 144 south. Mark mileage at the southern city limit sign. From that point go 4.2 miles to a lengthy road cut where good collecting is possible.

Rockhounding: Granbury is at the heart of a Lower Cretaceous formation rich in fossils. To the north of town there is a predominance of snails (Turritella), while south of town, the chief finds are oysters. Do not rule out Pennsylvanian era specimens such as trilobites here, however. The author recovered an incomplete trilobite at the site on TX 144.

Not to be missed here is Dinosaur Valley State Park near Glen Rose. The park contains the best preserved dinosaur tracks in the state. Tracks of the thirty-ton sauropod are found embedded in the solid rock bed of the Paluxy River. Tracks left by two other varieties of dinosaur also are found here.

To get to the park from Granbury take TX 144 south to U.S. Highway 67. Turn west towards Glen Rose. At the western edge of Glen Rose turn northwest on Farm Road 205. The park is located approximately 2.8 miles from the turn.

The nuclear power plant near Glen Rose also is said to have a nice display that is open to the public, showing fossils and dinosaur tracks.

SITE 34 GRANBURY FOSSILS

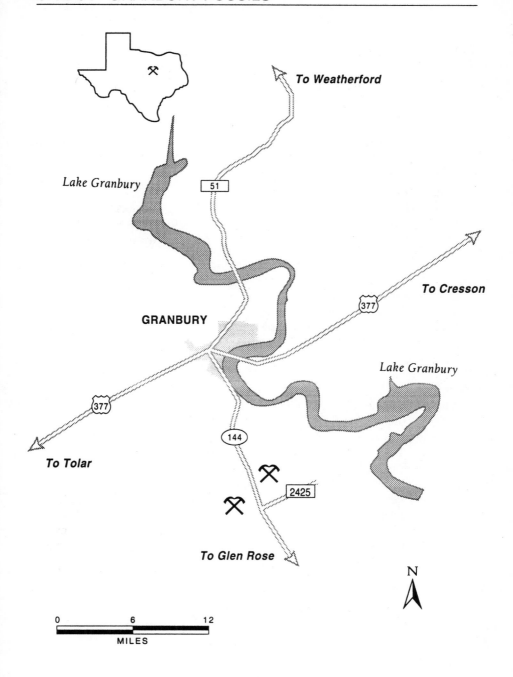

To Weatherford

Lake Granbury

51

To Cresson

377

GRANBURY

Lake Granbury

377

To Tolar

144

2425

To Glen Rose

N

0   6   12
MILES

SITE 35 *AGATE AND FLINT NEAR STERLING CITY*

Land type: Hills and mesas.

Elevation: 2,294 feet.

Best season: Late summer.

Land manager: Texas Department of Transportation.

Material: Flint, agate.

Tools: Hammer, chisels.

Vehicle: Any.

Accommodations: Motels are scarce; RV parking at E.V. Spence Reservoir.

Special attraction: E.V. Spence Reservoir.

Finding the site: Sterling City is located on U.S. Highway 87 between Big Spring and San Angelo. Good road cut collecting is found twenty miles east of Sterling City on Texas Highway 158 as well as twenty-three miles west of town, also on TX 158.

Rockhounding: It is often the unexpected finds that bring the most pleasure. Thus it was truly a joy for the author to find these road cuts bearing beautiful blue-banded flint and agate. The cut to the east of town is mostly float material, and contains more flint than agate, but nice pieces are possible.

The western site is a cut through solid rock that bears veins of the flint. While collectors seeking only the best material will slave for hours chiseling chunks from the wall, those who are less industrious will certainly be content with the scraps left behind by road crews and other hounds. The majority of the material is flinty, but careful looking will produce pieces with greater transparency, enough to qualify the material as agate. Even the opaque flint is quite attractive however. Both materials are found in pieces large enough for a variety of uses.

Sterling City lies in the midst of the drop-off of the great High Plains. Along the seventy mile stretch between Garden City to the west and Robert Lee to the east, the elevation drops about 900 feet. As you travel through the area, the rock seen in the road cuts change from light-colored Lower Cretaceous sediment to the red beds of the Permian era and back again . Though not abundant, fossils are possible in either formation.

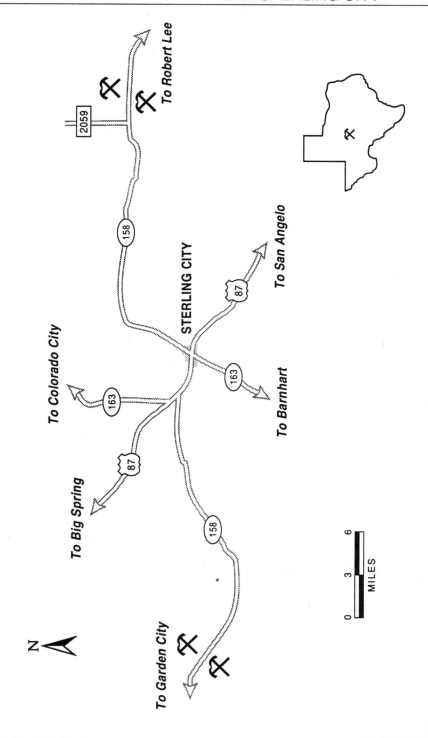

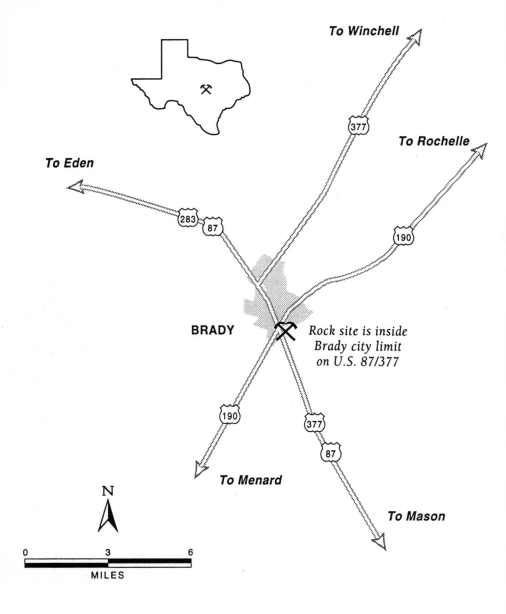

To Winchell

377

To Rochelle

To Eden

283 87

190

BRADY

Rock site is inside
Brady city limit
on U.S. 87/377

190

377

87

To Menard

To Mason

N

0   3   6
MILES

SITE 36 *BRADY FOSSILS*

Land type: Plains and hills.

Elevation: 1,670 feet.

Best season: Any.

Land manager: Texas Department of Transportation.

Material: Fossils.

Tools: None.

Vehicle: Any.

Accommodations: RV parking and motels in Brady.

Special attractions: Indian pictographs at Paint Rock, Caverns of Sonora.

Finding the site: Brady is located slightly north of the Texas hill country, at the junction of U.S. highways 87, 283, 377, and 190. The collecting site is approximately one-half-mile north of the southern city limit on U.S. 87/ 377. Look for a road cut consisting mainly of light tan, caliche-looking rock.

Crinoid and bryozoa stems are plentiful near Brady.

At the northern end on the east side of the road is an area of darker rocks, where the fossils are most abundant.

Rockhounding: There isn't much that needs to be said about this site except an appeal to take limited quantities, so that others might enjoy the fun as well. The ground here looks much as you would expect the floor of the sea to appear after a mass explosion. The fossils are so abundant, that in places, the soil beneath is almost completely hidden.

The specimens here are Pennsylvanian, chiefly crinoids, corals, and bryozoans. While crinoid stems account for the largest portion of the mass, careful searching could produce crinoid heads, cephalopods, and trilobites. (In a short search, the author recovered a partial crinoid head and a nice cephalopod specimen.)

Northwest of Brady, in the town of Paint Rock, excursions can be arranged to see pictographs painted on the limestone cliffs bordering the Concho River. The paintings span a time ranging from prehistoric to the end of the nineteenth century. For more information call 915-658-8250 or 915-655-4434.

Also of interest near here are the Caverns of Sonora. They are perhaps the most beautiful caverns in the southwestern United States. See the introductory section of this book titled, "Sights to See," for more information.

SITE 37 *COLORADO RIVER FOSSILS*

Land type: Rolling hills.
Elevation: 1,025 feet.
Best season: Late summer.
Land manager: Lower Colorado River Authority.
Material: Fossils, petrified wood, flint.
Tools: Pick, hammer.
Vehicle: Any
Accommodations: RV parking and motels within 25 miles.
Special attraction: Lake Buchanan.
Finding the site: Lampasas is located at the junction of U.S. highways 183 and 281, about twenty-eight miles west of Kileen. From Lampasas take Farm Road 580 west to the tiny town of Bend. Mark mileage at the western city limit sign. Go 1.1 miles. Turn right onto an unmarked road of black shale leading down to the river's edge. (If you pass the white fences of the ME Ranch, you've gone too far.)

Rockhounding: This is not a stop-and-go kind of site. Serious fossil hounds only need to give this one a try. The fossils here can be worth the search, but only if you have lots of time. The matrix rock here is Pennsylvanian shale from the Smithwick formation. Fossils found here include trilobites,

SITE 37   COLORADO RIVER FOSSILS
SITE 38   FLINT NEAR BEND

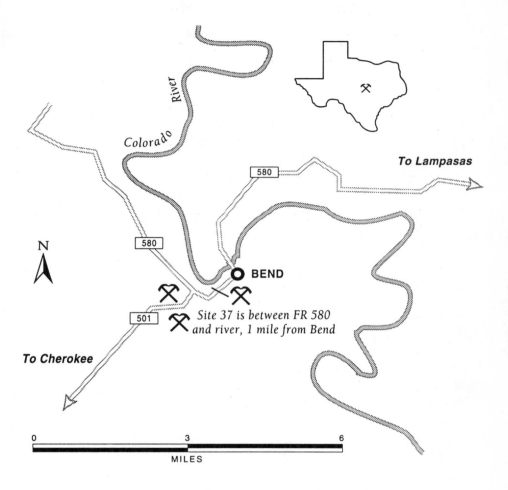

Site 37 is between FR 580 and river, 1 mile from Bend

cephalopods, and some very interesting gastropods.

The problem here is the availability of the specimens; they are encased between the layers of shale. Finding the good ones requires painstakingly splitting the layers in broken pieces of rock.

If your luck (or your patience) runs out, wander close to the hillside away from the river bed to look for petrified wood and flint. While both are somewhat limited, the flint specimens bear interesting patterns, and are nice for tumbling.

SITE 38 *FLINT NEAR BEND*

Land type: Rolling hills.
Elevation: 1,025 feet.
Best season: Late summer.
Land manager: Texas Department of Transportation.
Material: Flint, jasper.
Tools: Shovel.
Vehicle: Any.
Accommodations: RV parking and motels within 25 miles.
Special attraction: Lake Buchanan.
Finding the site: The tiny town of Bend is located about twenty-six miles west of Lampasas on Farm Road 580. From Bend, take FR 580 2.8 miles to Farm Road 501 and turn right. At 0.2 miles from the junction look for a rocky road cut on both sides of the road.

Rockhounding: Bright red jasper pebbles blend here with black-spotted flint for a pleasing combination of tumbling material. An occasional find of a larger piece worthy of cutting is possible with some digging. Not to be overlooked is the possibility of petrified wood or Pennsylvanian era fossils.

Much of the material presents a weathered reddish exterior, so careful examination is necessary to find the good stuff.

SITE 39 *LAMPASAS FOSSILS*

Land type: Rolling hills.
Elevation: 1,025 feet.
Best season: Late summer.
Land manager: Texas Department of Transportation.
Material: Fossils.
Tools: Shovel.
Vehicle: Any.
Accommodations: RV parking and motels in Lampasas.
Special attraction: Lake Buchanan.
Finding the site: Lampasas is located at the junction of U.S. highways 183 and 281 about twenty-eight miles west of Kileen. From Lampasas travel south on U.S. 183. Good collecting begins just south of the city limit and continues for approximately fifteen miles. Look for road side areas with loose beige rocky material.

Rockhounding: Lower Cretaceous fossils, mainly oysters, and lots of interesting root castings are found along the road south of Lampasas. While not as plentiful as in other areas, some good specimens can be found here.

Pennsylvanian and Mississippian era fossils should not be ruled out in this area, due to the close proximity of rocks from these periods. Possible finds from these eras would include trilobites and cephalopods. Any site bearing the telltale sign of crinoid stems is worth further investigation in the hopes of finding more valuable prizes.

Sampling numerous sites along the road seems to be the best way to operate here, since erosion at any given time can unearth or temporarily hide treasures. Careful digging might also produce good results.

SITE 39   *LAMPASAS FOSSILS*

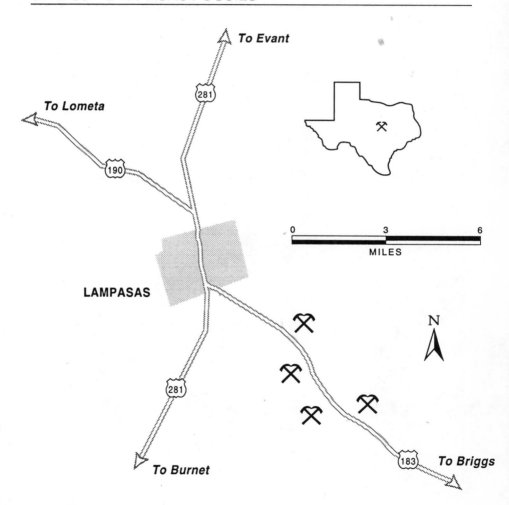

SITE 40 *MASON COUNTY TOPAZ*

Land type: Hills.

Elevation: 1,550 feet.

Best season: Late summer.

Land manager: Texas Department of Transportation.

Material: Topaz, smoky quartz.

Tools: Shovels, screens, water.

Vehicle: Any.

Accommodations: RV parking and motels in Mason.

Special attraction: Enchanted Rock.

Finding the site: Mason is located on U.S. Highway 87 at the northern edge of the hill country. From Mason take U.S. 87/377 north for about six miles to where the road crosses a sandy creek bed. Collecting is allowed along the creek near the road, provided no fences are crossed. (See map on page 92.)

Rockhounding: If gemstones are your thing, you're in the right place. Mason County is widely known for its cache of topaz in colors ranging from smoky gray to the prized sky blue. Smoky quartz is also found here, often in quite large crystals.

The gemstones form in the pegmatite dikes that course through the re-

Mason County topaz is often found in broken chunks of the pegmatite in which it forms.

gion and are then washed downhill to stream beds like this one, which is a tributary to Katemcy Creek.

Finding the good stuff requires time and patience as you sift through the sands of the stream bed. Quartz is abundant but look for good crystal formation. The topaz is often difficult to distinguish from the quartz and quartz-laden rocks until cleaned, so take along a water source to do some on-site washing. It could mean the difference between tossing aside a gem and taking it home.

Keep the field characteristics of topaz in mind as you hunt. It can be white, colorless, pink, or bluish. It has a colorless streak compared to the white streak of quartz. It has a Mohs hardness of eight, compared to quartz with a hardness of seven. When in doubt, identify a piece of quartz (or take a known sample with you) then use it for scratch testing. It will not scratch the topaz, but the topaz will scratch it, as will other quartz samples.

The best field characteristic of the topaz, and the reason for washing all suspects, is the perfect cleavage it presents in one direction. This creates a smooth, glass-like sheen on broken surfaces not usually found on quartz.

This particular site is intended for hounds with short attention spans, casual lookers, or those with little time to seek the treasure. While topaz is found here (the author recovered a nice specimen quality piece in a very short time), it is probably not the best place to look. It just happens to be accessible. For the serious topaz seeker, there are two ranches nearby that offer full days of hunting for a moderate fee. See sites 42 and 43 for more information.

SITE 41 *MASON COUNTY AGATE AND FLINT*

Land type: Rolling hills.

Elevation: 1,550 feet.

Best season: Late summer.

Land manager: Texas Department of Transportation.

Material: Flint, agate.

Tools: None.

Vehicle: Any.

Accommodations: RV parking and motels in Mason.

Special attraction: Enchanted Rock.

Finding the site: From Mason take U.S. Highway 87/377 north about 5.4 miles to a rocky road cut on both sides of the road. Collecting is also possible in other cuts for about four miles.

Rockhounding: Ever hear of Mason County flint and agate? Of course you haven't. It is almost completely overlooked because everybody wants to get at the topaz. But if you get tired of looking for gemstones stop at this site for a refreshing return to reality.

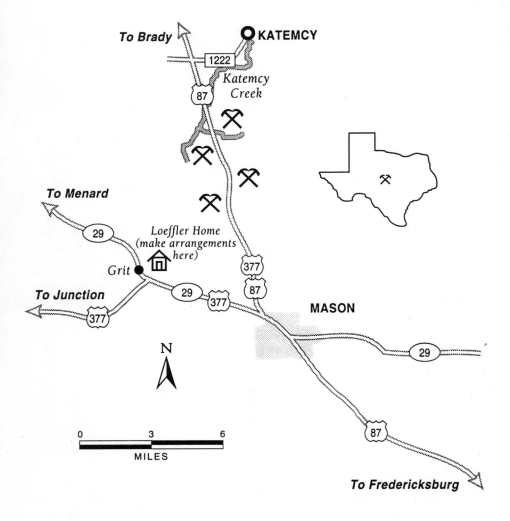

Some very nice pieces of dark flint, some of it almost black, are mixed with the same chocolate brown agate and flint found along the southern edges of the hill country. A few pieces are also banded with solid white. It is all float material, and presents a heavily coated and weathered exterior, so look carefully, and take home a few samples that are doubtful. They may just surprise you.

Pieces range in size from pebbles to fist-sized cobbles. The smaller chocolate colored pieces tumble nicely and look almost good enough to eat when finished. Keep a sharp eye out for worked pieces of the flint here as well. Arrowheads and spearpoints are relatively common throughout the hill country.

This is very serious deer hunting territory. Do not venture away from major highways at any time between November and the first week of January. An archery season also runs throughout the month of October.

Quartz crystals are found in Mason County.

SITES 42 & 43 *TOPAZ AT THE SEQUIST AND HOFFMAN RANCHES*

Land type: Rolling hills.

Elevation: 1,550 feet.

Best season: Late summer.

Land manager: Mrs. Wesley Loeffler.

Material: Topaz.

Tools: Hammer, chisels, picks, shovels, screens.

Vehicle: Utility.

Accommodations: RV parking and motels in Mason.

Special attraction: Enchanted Rock State Natural Area.

Finding the site: Arrangements for hunting on both ranches must be made with Mrs. Loeffler in the tiny town of Grit. From Mason take U.S. Highway 377/29 about 4.7 miles to Grit. The Loeffler home is on the right side of the road. A portion of it used to be a country store, making it easy to spot. Look for the name Loeffler on the mail box out front. (See map on page 92).

Rockhounding: The Sequist and Hoffman ranches are currently the only two ranches open to rockhounds seeking the treasure of topaz in Mason County (unless you know somebody who knows somebody, etc.). Though open to collectors for years, beautiful stones are still there for hounds willing to work for them.

Rockhounds are asked to fill all holes they may dig, not destroy animals, plants, or fences, and pay in advance for the privilege of looking. The fee is currently $10 per day for ages ten and older, and $5 for ages six through nine. No half-day fees are allowed. Your permit will run for twenty four hours, meaning if you begin looking at four in the afternoon, you have until four the next day. The ranches are generally closed to rockhounds during deer hunting season.

Llanite boulders are piled beside Texas Highway 16 north of Llano.

SITE 44 *LLANITE, NO PLACE BUT LLANO COUNTY*

Land type: Rolling hills.
Elevation: 1,029 feet.
Best season: Late summer.
Land manager: Texas Department of Transportation.
Material: Llanite.
Tools: Chisels, hammer, gads, safety goggles.
Vehicle: Any.
Accommodations: RV parking and motels in Llano.
Special attractions: Enchanted Rock State Natural Area, fishing.
Finding the site: Llano is located in the northern hill country about seventy-six miles northwest of Austin. From Llano take Texas Highway 16 north for about 8.6 miles to a road cut bearing distinctive granite. If you pass a roadside picnic area, you've passed the Llanite.

Rockhounding: From a distance, Llanite looks much the same as the other pink granites found throughout this area. But a closer look reveals an important difference: beautiful blue quartz crystals. They twinkle from between the pink feidspar masses like tiny pools of water.

Reportedly, this particular combination of colors is not found in any other granite in the world. The mixture of pink and blue varies considerably from stone to stone, but all have the distinctive blue pools.

Many have mistakenly called the blue crystals agates. Quartz and agate are both forms of silicon dioxide (S_iO_2), but agate is microcrystalline in form, while quartz forms true crystals. Although the blue spots in the Llanite do resemble tiny agates encased in the granite, research has proven the silicon dioxide here to be a crystalline variety. As with any granite, the Llanite polishes well, and is ideally used as large items like bookends and desk sets. Collecting a good sample can present a problem, however. There is plenty of it at this roadside site, and it is likely to stay that way, because this stuff is hard with a capital "H." If you want more than palm-sized scraps found on the ground take serious tools, goggles, and lots of sweat.

SITE 45 *LLANO RIVER FLINT AND GRANITE*

Land type: Rolling hills.
Elevation: 1,029 feet.
Best season: Late summer.
Land manager: Public land.
Material: Flint, granite, quartz, fossils.
Tools: None.

SITE 44 *LLANITE, NO PLACE BUT LLANO COUNTY*
SITE 45 *LLANO RIVER FLINT AND GRANITE*

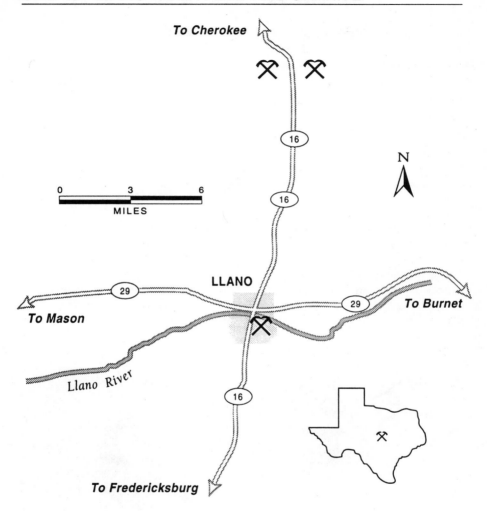

Vehicle: Any.

Accommodations: RV parking and motels in Llano.

Special attractions: Enchanted Rock State Natural Area, fishing.

Finding the site: Llano is located in the northern hill country about seventy-six miles northwest of Austin. In Llano, on Texas Highway 16, there is a bridge crossing the Llano River. On the west side is Llano City Lake, with the river on the east side of the bridge. At the south end of the bridge, turn east. Go past the library, then turn north onto a dirt road leading down to the river's edge.

Rockhounding: Ask anyone from Llano County where the best rock hunting is found (for anything other than Llanite) and the answer is likely to be the Llano River. Because it is considered a navigable waterway, the river is public property. The problem here is that the land adjacent to it is not, and nobody seems inclined to allow folks to cross their land to get to the river. The bridge in the town of Llano seems to offer the easiest access.

Once you find your way down to the river, which is a scrambled mix of sand bars, brush, and streams of water, the only limits on your hunting are how far your feet will carry you, and how much time you wish to spend.

At the access point, the take consists of granite chunks and flint. All along the river, the possibilities include arrowheads, fossils, granite, and quartz crystals. Because some of the land along the river outside of town is leased to hunters during deer season, hiking the river in winter is not recommended. Keep in mind also that brushy areas could be snake havens in warm weather, so take necessary precautions.

Flint from the Llano River often exhibits signs of chipping and flaking.

SITE 46 *BURNET COUNTY GRANITE*

Land type: Rolling hills.

Elevation: 1,319 feet.

Best season: Late summer.

Land manager: Texas Department of Transportation.

Material: Granite.

Tools: Chisels, hammer, gads.

Vehicle: Any.

Accommodations: RV parking and motels around lake area, and in Burnet.

Special attraction: Longhorn Cavern State Park.

Restrictions: No collecting allowed inside state parks, or along state park roads.

Finding the site: Burnet is located on U.S. Highway 281 about twenty-two miles south of Lampasas. From Burnet go west on Texas Highway 29 toward the Buchanan Dam. Granite can be collected in numerous road cuts along this road. One of the best sites is about 150 yards east of the Inks Lake Bridge.

Rockhounding: This area of the state is famous for two things: a chain of lakes along the Colorado River that provides recreation, power, and drinking water to surrounding towns; and granite. Though much of the granite is pink in color, occasional outcroppings of white, gray, and black can be seen as well.

This region is known geologically as the Llano Uplift. The rocks are probably the oldest in the state (1.35 billion years). They are exposed as the result of an upward push that occurred millions of years ago along deeply buried fault zones, combined with powerful erosion.

The granite is quarried for architectural uses throughout the area, with lesser quality deposits being used in road material. For the collector, the stone takes a nice polish, and is best used in large scale pieces such as bookends, desk sets, and small sculptures. Examples of the granite in use can be seen throughout the state, including the state capitol building in Austin, which is built from the familiar pink stone.

A nice diversion in the area is provided by a trip to Longhorn Caverns State Park. The cave provides a look not only deep into the geological history of the area but into more recent times as well. It was once operated as a saloon and dance hall. The drive along Park Road 4, which loops between Texas Highway 29 west of Burnet and U.S. 281 south of Marble Falls, is quite a scenic drive, even if you don't plan to stop at the caverns. The road passes Inks Lake State Park, and numerous outcroppings of granite are scattered along the route. Take pictures here but no rocks. Collecting is prohibited along State Park roads.

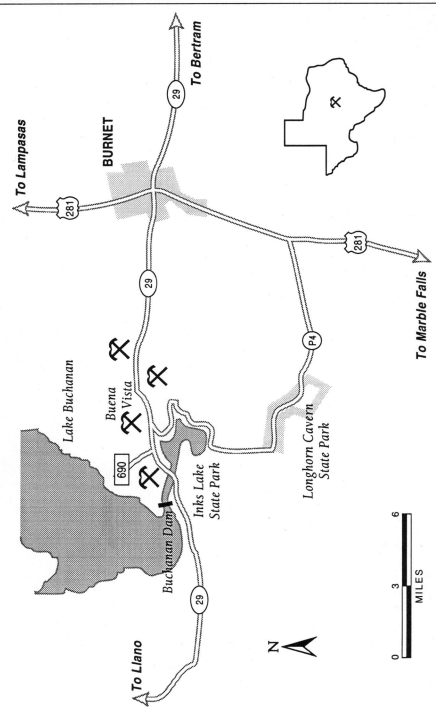

SITE 47 GRAVELS NEAR MARBLE FALLS

Land type: Rolling hills.

Elevation: 764 feet.

Best season: Late summer.

Land manager: Texas Department of Transportation.

Material: Agate, flint, jasper, quartzite.

Tools: Water.

Vehicle: Any.

Accommodations: RV parking and motels in Marble Falls.

Special attraction: Pedernales Falls State Park.

Finding the site: Marble Falls is located in the midst of the lake region on U.S. Highway 281. From Marble Falls take U.S. 281 south 1.9 miles to Ranch Road 2147. Turn east and travel for about 3.4 miles. Look for an exposed gravel bed on the north side of the road. Note: the westward branch of RR 2147 is more than a mile north of the eastbound branch.

Rockhounding: The heart of the Llano Uplift region seems an unlikely place to find a mass of gravels and cobbles like the one found at this site. Most likely, these are river rocks, washed here by some long-ago flood of the nearby Colorado River.

Whatever their source, they present a fun place to spend the afternoon for any rockhound. The booty includes traces of chocolate colored agate, flint in pink, gray, and black, fiery red and caramel-colored jasper, and quartzite in all colors.

The only tool necessary for collecting here is perhaps some water for washing the heavy soils from the rocks. Because these are river rocks, many of the agate and flint nodules will have rough, weathered exteriors. Choose carefully, looking for chipped areas that may hold clues to the goodies inside.

SITE 47 GRAVELS NEAR MARBLE FALLS

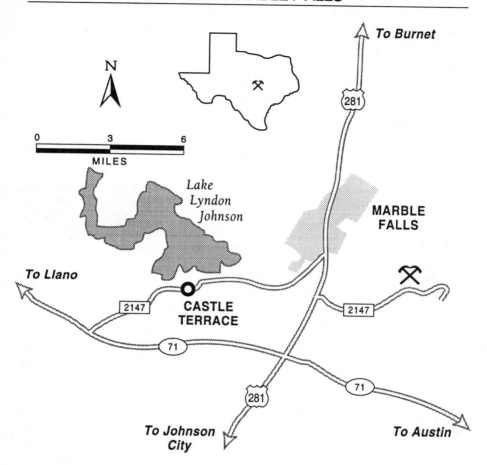

SITE 48 *JOHNSON CITY FLINT*

Land type: Rolling hills.

Elevation: 1,197 feet.

Best season: Late summer.

Land manager: Texas Department of Transportation.

Material: Flint.

Tools: Chisels, hammer, pick, safety goggles.

Vehicle: Any.

Accommodations: RV parking and motels within 5 miles.

Special attraction: Pedernales Falls State Park.

Finding the site: Johnson City is located at the junction of U.S.highways 290 west and 281, about sixty-five miles north of San Antonio. From Johnson City travel north on U.S. 281 for about 3.3 miles. Look for a very rocky road cut. Most of the flint is found on the west side of the road.

Rockhounding: Some very interesting flint is found in this road cut just north of Johnson City. It is a combination of solid white and creamy brown. The white has a slightly different texture, probably due to minor impurities. There are also tiny quartz stringers throughout the larger pieces.

At first glance, this material would not seem suitable for much, other than specimen collecting. Do not be fooled, however. When polished, the difference in hardness creates an illusion between the brown and white material. The brown seems to float above the white, and the quartz crystal stringers add flash, making these pieces very attractive.

There are some loose scraps to be found on the ground, but choice selections are imbedded in the wall of the road cut. Fortunately it chisels out without too much difficulty.

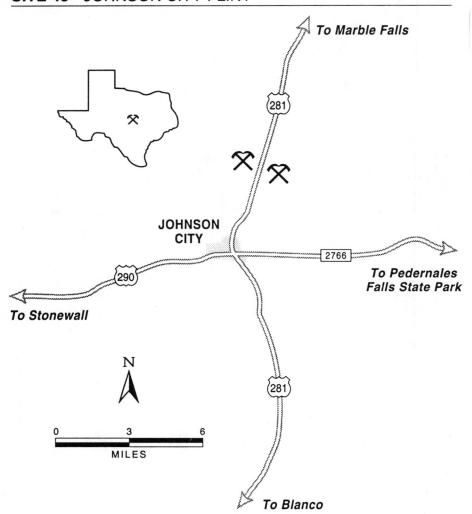

To Marble Falls

281

JOHNSON
CITY

2766

To Pedernales
Falls State Park

290

To Stonewall

N

0   3   6
MILES

281

To Blanco

SITE 49 STONEWALL FLINT AND AGATE

Land type: Hills.
Elevation: 1,512 feet.
Best season: Late summer.
Land manager: Texas Department of Transportation.
Material: Flint and agate.
Tools: None.
Vehicle: Any.
Accommodations: RV parking and motels within 15 miles.
Special attractions: Peaches, LBJ State and National Historical Sites.
Finding the site: Stonewall is located 13.5 miles east of Fredericksburg on U.S. Highway 290. From Stonewall take U.S. 290 east. Begin looking for any areas of erosion. Good collecting sites at the time of writing were at 1.8 and 3.9 miles east of Stonewall.

Rockhounding: This area has about as much good quality Gillespie County flint as you are likely to find anywhere. The colors include gray, brown, tan, and a golden caramel. A considerable portion of the gray material bears lovely striping of pink, white, and brown. As with many other hill country flint sites, there is a small quantity of agate here as well. It tends to be brown, much of it with gold and red swirls. The pieces with good clarity and depth are scarce though and take considerable patience to find.

SITE 49 STONEWALL FLINT AND AGATE

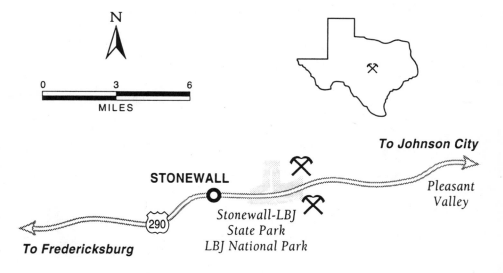

The trick to finding a good site here is to find any area of erosion. Weed growth and drainage play a huge role in the availability of good road side hunting. There are several ranches along this road that seem to have large quantities of surface rocks. A quick drive up to a farmhouse could result in being allowed to gather all you can haul.

Be sure to save room to haul away some peaches, however. The peaches from this area are some of the best grown in the state. Roadside collecting is possible at numerous fruit stands throughout the area.

Also of interest here is the LBJ Ranch and National Historical Site. In order to tour the ranch, you must board buses at the State Historical Site on U.S. 290.

SITE 50 *FREDERICKSBURG FLINT AND AGATE*

Land type: Rolling hills.

Elevation: 1,743 feet.

Best season: Late summer.

Land manager: Texas Department of Transportation.

Material: Flint and agate.

Tools: None.

Vehicle: Any.

Accommodations: RV parking, motels, and bed-and-breakfasts in Fredericksburg.

Special attractions: Shopping, Enchanted Rock State Natural Area.

For more information: Send $2 for a copy of the Fredericksburg Standard Radio Post, P.O. Box 473, Fredericksburg, TX 78624. It is a visitor's guide packed with everything you need to know about Fredericksburg.

Finding the site: Fredericksburg is located on U.S. Highway 87, about seventy-five miles north of San Antonio. From Fredericksburg take Farm Road 965 north toward Enchanted Rock State Natural Area. Good collecting begins alongside the road about 2.4 miles from the city limit and continues for roughly ten miles.

Rockhounding: The flint characteristic of Gillespie County is quite plentiful on this scenic drive to Enchanted Rock. The color is usually gray, some with very nice variegations. An occasional small piece of petrified wood can also be found here. Agate hounds with sharp eyes can also find quality pieces suitable for tumbling along this road. Some of the agate is the chocolate brown found farther south near Bandera and Devine, but a few nice white and gray pieces are possible as well.

Though the rocks for collecting are somewhat less than stunning here, this road will lead you to Texas' biggest, most unusual, and most sought after rock: Enchanted Rock. It was believed by many Indian tribes to hold supernatural powers. Others told of human sacrifices from the top of the

Farm Road 965 provides collecting opportunities on the way to Enchanted Rock.

SITE 50   *FREDERICKSBURG FLINT AND AGATE*

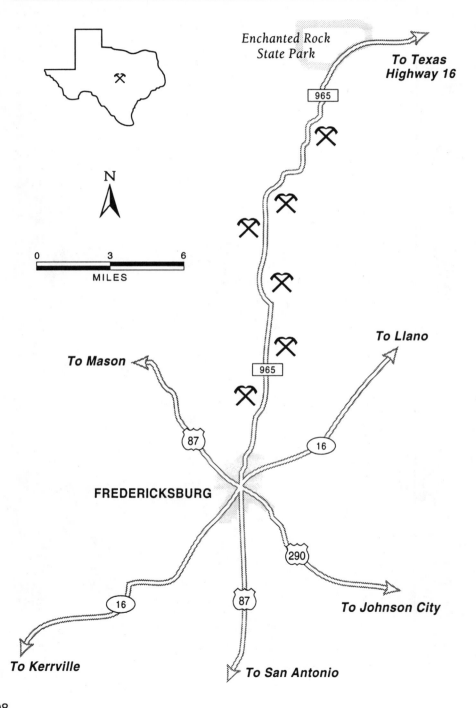

Enchanted Rock
State Park

To Texas
Highway 16

965

N

0   3   6
MILES

To Llano

To Mason

965

87

16

FREDERICKSBURG

290

16

87

To Johnson City

To Kerrville

To San Antonio

five-hundred-foot granite dome.

Visitors today are more likely to be enchanted by the sheer magnitude and beauty of the pink rock. Climbing it is an accomplishment talked about by every visitor from age three to eighty-three. The hike to the top requires neither special climbing skills, nor gear. Just a good pair of non- skid shoes or boots and the desire to get to the top. (The author even has a relative who is quite afraid of heights who made it.)

Almost everyone who visits here leaves with a different feeling for the place. Perhaps it's the power of suggestion in the name. Perhaps it is simply a renewed appreciation for the grandeur of nature. Or perhaps it really is enchanted.

Now if we're talking about enchanting, as opposed to enchanted, the streets of Fredericksburg certainly qualify. From crafts to antiques, from rock shops to German restaurants, this town will likely steal your heart. Historic "Sunday Houses," built so that farm and ranch residents could spend weekends in town, line the street. Many now serve as bed-and-breakfast inns.

SITE 51 *KERRVILLE FLINT*

Land type: Rolling hills.

Elevation: 1,645 feet.

Best season: Late summer.

Land manager: Texas Department of Transportation.

Material: Flint, fossils.

Tools: None.

Vehicle: Any.

Accommodations: RV parking, motels, and hotels in Kerrville.

Special attractions: Art museums, Kerrville State Park.

Finding the site: Kerrville is located just off Interstate Highway 10, sixty-six miles northwest of San Antonio. From Kerrville, take Texas Highway 16 north. Mark mileage at the junction of TX 16 and I-10. Go north 2.5 miles. Look for rocky road cuts on both sides of the road.

Rockhounding: Most of the flint found in this area is somewhat nondescript. The color is a blend of the gray found farther north in Gillespie County and the lovely brown found to the south. The real reason for stopping here is to seek pieces of pale gray flint with a slight hint of blue. The blue tends to wash out in sunlight, so it is advisable to take several samples of gray with you, to be examined indoors.

There are also some fossils to be found at this location, mostly tiny Turritella snails. The bulk of the fossils here will be found embedded in the tough limestone, but an occasional loose specimen is possible.

Kerrville is known statewide as a Mecca for western artists. Examples

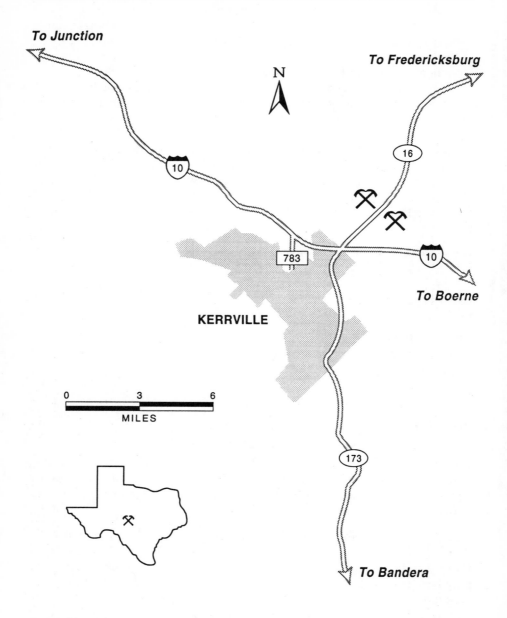

of western art can be seen throughout the town, and at the Cowboy Artists of America Museum located on Texas Highway 173. The Kerrville State Park is one of the prettiest the state has to offer, and comes complete with hundreds of semi-tame white-tailed deer.

SITE 52 *FOSSILS NORTH OF BANDERA*

Land type: Rolling hills.

Elevation: 1,258 feet.

Best season: Late summer.

Land manager: Texas Department of Transportation.

Material: Fossils.

Tools: None.

Vehicle: Any.

Accommodations: RV parking, motels, and "dude ranches" in Bandera.

Special attractions: Antique shopping, scenic drives.

For more information: Bandera Chamber of Commerce 512-796-4312.

Finding the site: Bandera is located at the junction of Texas highways 16 and 173. It is fifty miles northwest of San Antonio, and twenty-six miles south of Kerrville. From Bandera take TX 173 north. Good fossil collecting begins about six miles north of town and continues for four to six miles.

Rockhounding: Okay fossil hounds, this site is for you. The fossils here are some of the best preserved Lower Cretaceous specimens in the state. The clams are often complete; the Turritella snail shells look as if they could have been occupied yesterday. Both are preserved with enough detail to make species identification a breeze. There are also a few oysters here as well as several species of echinoids.

Fossils found near Bandera are some of the best-preserved in the state.

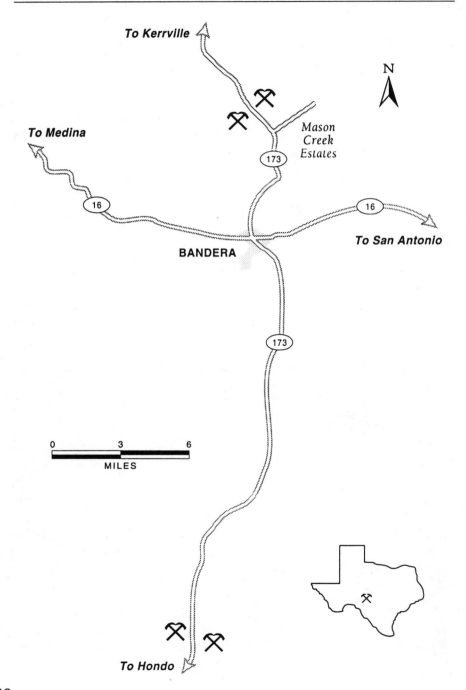

The fossils are found in the Glen Rose formation, which has a somewhat yellowish color in comparison to the gray Edwards limestone found above it. Look near the bottom of the road cuts in the loose, caliche-like material for the best finds.

Bandera is known as the "Cowboy Capital of the World." Visitors are encouraged to be a cowboy for a day at the many guest ranches in the area that offer horseback riding, roping lessons, and other cowboy adventures. Contact the Chamber of Commerce for listings of the ranches.

Bandera is also the central point for several of the state's most scenic drives. TX 173 north to Kerrville is the gateway to the Texas Hill Country, cutting through huge limestone hills. TX 16 west (which also ends up in Kerrville) meanders along through green valleys, crisscrossed by winding creeks.

SITE 53 *CHOCOLATE AGATE SOUTH OF BANDERA*

Land type: Rolling hills.
Elevation: 1,258 feet.
Best season: Late summer.
Land manager: Texas Department of Transportation.
Material: Agate, flint.
Tools: Hammer, chisels, pick, goggles.
Vehicle: Any.
Accommodations: RV parking, motels, and "dude ranches" in Bandera.
Special attractions: Antique shopping, scenic drives.
Finding the site: Bandera is located at the junction of Texas highways 16 and 173. It is about fifty miles northwest of San Antonio, and twenty-six miles south of Kerrville. From Bandera travel south on Texas Highway 173. About sixteen miles south of town there is a massive road cut through solid rock. Collecting is on both sides of the highway, but access is best on the east side.

Rockhounding: Just as you enter the Texas Hill Country, south of Bandera is a road cut that offers flint and agate freshly chiseled from the wall of rock in which they formed. Both materials are chiefly chocolate brown, although some golden caramel color is evidenced here as well. (It's enough to make your mouth water isn't it?) Finding pieces with true clarity and banding that qualify as agate is somewhat difficult, but even the pieces that are opaque are beautiful. Both materials often bear swirls of red and gold.

There are some scrap pieces to be found on the ground, but the best stuff will require some labor. Pieces ranging in sizes of up to fifteen pounds are possible with a little hard work. For those who haven't the time nor the inclination to break out a hammer and chisel, see Site 65 for a description of a site bearing the same lovely material, only in the form of loose float.

This agate- and flint-bearing roadcut frames the entrance to the "Hill Country."

SITE 54 *LAKE SOMERVILLE WOOD AND JASPER*

Land type: Rolling hills.

Elevation: 250 feet.

Best season: Late summer, fall.

Land manager: City of Somerville.

Material: Jasper, flint, wood, calcite crystals, tektites.

Tools: None.

Vehicle: Any.

Accommodations: RV parking at the lake, motels within 20 miles.

Special attraction: Blue Bell Creameries ice cream factory in Brenham.

Restrictions: No collecting allowed inside nearby state parks.

Finding the site: Lake Somerville is located just off of Texas Highway 36, southwest of Bryan/College Station. In the town of Somerville turn west from TX 36 onto Thornberry Drive. Go 1.5 miles to the lake entrance. Proceed to the top of the dam, then turn right. Collecting is allowed in Rocky Park, which is directly below and to the north of the dam.

Rockhounding: The area surrounding Lake Somerville is widely known as a collecting site for tektites, which are glassy, black stones suspected of being meteorites. Unfortunately, they are quite scarce. While looking for the elusive space rocks, why not enjoy the feast of petrified wood and brightly colored jasper found among the hills of Rocky Park?

The booty includes some very interesting stuff. There are fist-sized pieces of petrified wood, though most of it is specimen quality only.(Close inspection of smaller pieces though, will turn up wood with silica content high enough for good color and polish.) There is brilliant red jasper, and some very interesting groupings of calcite crystals as well.

While many of same types of rocks could be found surrounding the entire lake, Rocky Park is just about the only legitimate collecting area. Much of the land around the lake is privately owned, with the rest being incorporated by state parks. No collecting is allowed inside the state parks.

SITE 54 LAKE SOMERVILLE WOOD AND JASPER

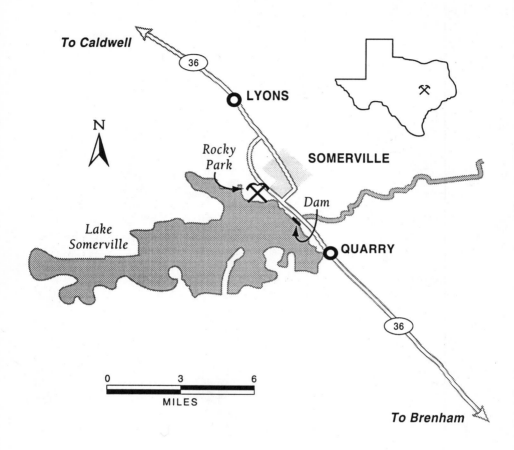

To Caldwell

36

LYONS

N

Rocky
Park

SOMERVILLE

Dam

Lake
Somerville

QUARRY

36

0   3   6
MILES

To Brenham

SITE 55 *LEDBETTER WOOD AND JASPER*

Land type: Rolling hills.

Elevation: 350 feet.

Best season: Late summer.

Land manager: Texas Department of Transportation.

Material: Petrified wood, jasper, flint.

Tools: None.

Vehicle: Any.

Accommodations: RV parking and motels within 25 miles.

Special attraction: Fishing at Lake Somerville.

Finding the site: Ledbetter is located on U.S. Highway 290 about sixty-two miles east of Austin. From Ledbetter take Farm Road 1291 south about two miles. Good collecting is found in the drainage ditches along both sides of the road for the next two miles.

Rockhounding: Wood, wood, and more wood. The supply of petrified wood mixed into this mass of what appears to be river rocks seems almost endless. The pieces range in size from one to eight inches in length. Most of the material has a high silica content, and exhibits some color, making it suitable for cutting and polishing. While most of the wood is unidentifiable, there is a small quantity of palm wood to be found here.

The jasper and flint are of mixed variety. There is a nice supply of red, gray, and even some of the brown found farther to the west near Devine and Bandera. Of course, where there is a large quantity of silica-based material like the flint and jasper, never rule out the possibility of agates. The author recovered a fist-sized piece of chocolate brown agate with exceptional clarity, accented with white banding.

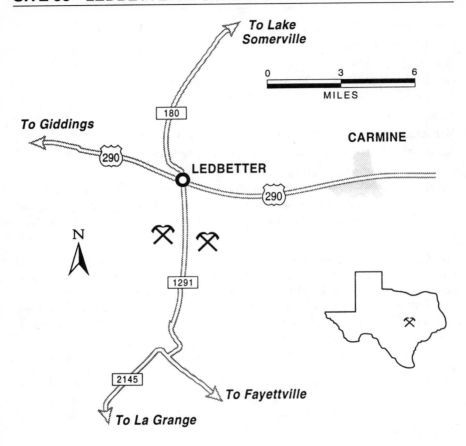

SITE 56 *LA GRANGE WOOD AND JASPER*

Land type: Rolling hills.

Elevation: 272 feet.

Best season: Late summer.

Land manager: Fayette County.

Material: Petrified wood, jasper, agate.

Tools: Shovel.

Vehicle: Utility.

Accommodations: RV parking and motels within 15 miles.

Special attractions: Fayette Herritage Museum and Archives.

Finding the site: La Grange is located near the junction of U.S. Highway 77 and Texas Highway 71, about sixty-two miles southeast of Austin. From La Grange take US 77 north for about six miles to Fayette County Road 148. Turn east. Go 1.2 miles to Fayet County Road 152. Turn north. Look for cobbles along the sides of this road, especially when the road is freshly graded.

Rockhounding: The area surrounding La Grange is some of the rockiest land in the state. The mixture of large cobbles found here contains large supplies of petrified wood, jasper, and small quantities of agate. Petrified palm wood is the chief goal of most hounds who collect in the area.

Though not overly plentiful, the palm wood is here. Don't limit yourself to looking for tiny pieces, specimens roughly the size of footballs have been found in this area. It is for this reason that shovels are highly useful. Pieces of this size are not often just lying on the surface.

Though the county roads are generally passable, variable weather conditions can quickly create large mudholes and ruts (and all those rocks don't help either). Therefore, pickup trucks or other high-clearance vehicles are recommended.

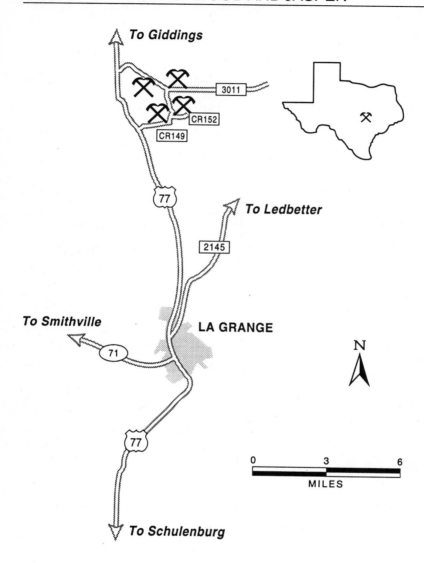

SITE 57 *SMITHVILLE WOOD AND JASPER*

Land type: Rolling hills.

Elevation: 324 feet.

Best season: Late summer.

Land manager: Texas Department of Transportation.

Material: Wood, flint, agate, jasper.

Tools: Shovel.

Vehicle: Any.

Accommodations: RV parking and motels within 10 miles.

Special attraction: Buescher State Park.

Finding the site: Smithville is located on Texas Highway 71, forty-two miles southeast of Austin. In Smithville take Farm Road 153 north for about 2.5 miles. Cobble beds suitable for collecting are found in the drainage ditches along both sides of the road for the next quarter mile.

Rockhounding: Petrified wood, various colors of flint, agate, and jasper can all be found in the cobbles scattered throughout this area, with palm wood being the main treasure to seek. Remember that though the palm wood is easily identified by its dotted cross section, this often requires ideal lighting, clean rocks, and even cutting. If your goal is only palm wood, always take home a few of the pieces that are doubtful. Even a practiced eye can be fooled in the field.

Nearby Buescher State Park contains a forest of what are known as "the lost pines." They are so named because they are separated from the nearest pine forests by more than one hundred miles. It is quite interesting that petrified palm wood is found near both forests, but rarely found in between. It would seem that there was once an area of lost palm trees as well.

SITE 57 *SMITHVILLE WOOD AND JASPER*

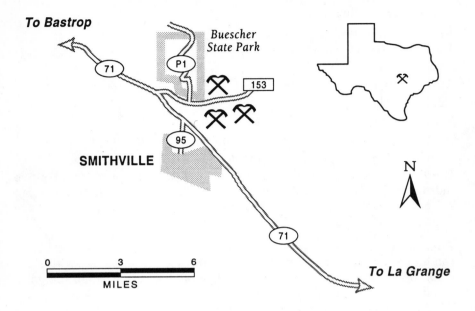

To Bastrop

Buescher
State Park

71

P1

153

95

SMITHVILLE

71

To La Grange

N

0   3   6
MILES

EAST TEXAS

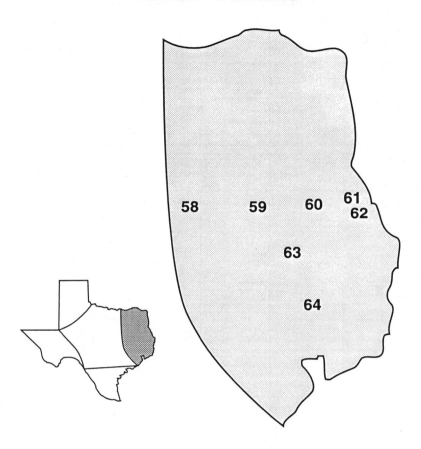

OVERVIEW

Collecting in the eastern portion of the state centers almost entirely on wood. While numerous varieties abound here, the number one goal sought by most collectors is petrified palm wood. Because palm falls into the plant group known as monocots, this wood is easily identifiable. Rather than continuous xylem and phloem tubes that ring the tree, the vascular system of a monocot is composed of pairs of the tubes bundled together throughout the plant tissue. A cross section of palm wood reveals these pairs as small dots in the wood. The palm wood is generally gray, brown, black, or a combination of these colors. An occasional piece will exhibit red, orange, and even blue, however. There also are fossils to be found in the region, primarily along the northern and western edges.

Roadside collecting is possible in a few places but is entirely limited to areas of erosion. Lush ground cover prevents collecting in many areas. Large quantities of wood are found in the national forests in this region. It is debatable whether or not collecting is allowed on the federal land. As any local resident can tell you, these forests are not preserves for the pine trees growing here. They are harvested and replanted in the same manner as the privately owned land. Research conducted by the author turned up neither a written restriction on collecting, nor clear cut permission. Therefore, no sites are listed here within the national forests, and no recommendations to collect there are given.

Private property collecting is possible, but many variables must be considered by both the land owner and the collector. Timber cutting, gravel quarrying, and game hunting all restrict the time and location for collecting. For current information, the best source of information is Otis Johnson, of Indian Springs. For more information on Mr. Johnson see Site 64.

Game hunting seasons restrict safe collecting more than the weather. Dense forest growth resricts visability and makes even a quick stop along the side of the road risky during hunting season. Summer temperatures are not unbearable, but high humidity can make lengthy collecting trips quite uncomfortable. Early spring (March) and late summer (August, September) would seem to be the best times if you can avoid seasonal downpours.

SITE 58 *FOSSILS AND WOOD NEAR KOSSE*

Land type: Forest.

Elevation: 383 feet.

Best season: Early spring, late summer.

Land manager: Texas Department of Transportation.

Material: Fossils and petrified wood.

Tools: None.

Vehicle: Any.

Accommodations: RV parking and motels in Groesbeck.

Special attractions: Fort Parker State Park.

Finding the site: Kosse is located at the intersection of Texas highways 14 and 7, southeast of Waco. From Kosse take TX 7 east for 11.6 miles. Look for road cuts on both sides of the road bearing erroded sandstone beds.

Rockhounding: Paleocene epoch fossils and small wood sections abound in this eroded sandstone bed between Kosse and Marquez. The fossils are predominately bivalves and gastropods, and many are quite well preserved. The wood is specimen quality, mostly lacking enough silica content to polish suitably.

Kosse is situated just to the east of a division between Upper Cretaceous formations and the more recent Lower Tertiary, which includes the Pale-

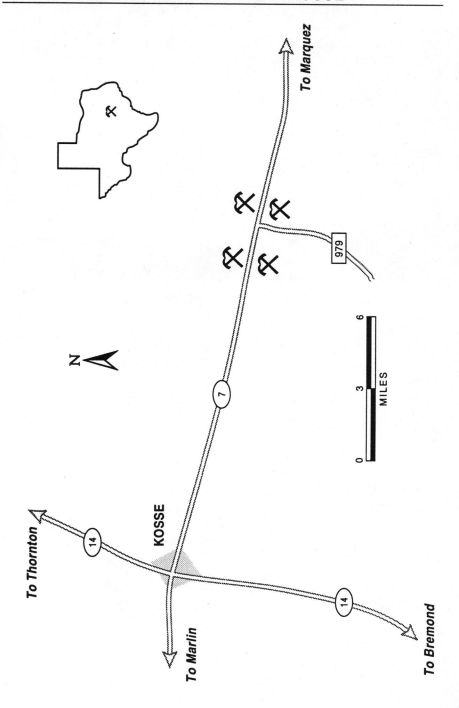

Paleocene epoch clams and wood found near Kosse.

ocene and Eocene epochs. The Lower Tertiary extends east to the Lousiana border, and southwest to the Mexican border between Del Rio and Laredo. It is overlayed to the southeast by more recent sedimentary rocks of the Upper Tertiary, Pleistocene, and Holocene periods.

The sandy soils and relatively light forestation of the area near Kosse create an erosional opportunity for the fossils from this period to be exposed. Farther east, as the pine forests grow dense, these fossils become more difficult to find.

For fishing and camping nearby, the tiny lake at Fort Parker State Park is ideal. It is one of the few lakes in East Texas that is not cluttered with housing developements. The deer and water fowl are abundant, and the scenery is supurb.

SITE 59 *PETRIFIED PALM NEAR CROCKETT*

Land type: Pine forest.

Elevation: 350 feet.

Best season: Early spring, late summer.

Land manager: Texas Department of Transportation.

Material: Wood and jasper.

Tools: Rake, rock pick, water.

Vehicle: Any.

Accommodations: RV parking and motels within 10 miles.

Special attractions: Davy Crockett National Forest.

Finding the site: Crockett is located at the junction of U.S. Highway 287 and Texas highways 7, 21, and 19. It is about 117 miles north of Houston. From Crockett travel south on TX 19, looking for areas of erosion. Any rocky area should be inspected. There are numerous county roads that intersect TX 19. These may or may not prove fruitful, depending upon vegetation conditions at the time.

Rockhounding: Rock hunting in East Texas makes you wish you'd brought along a gas powered garden tiller. The ground is either covered with eight inches of pine needles, lush grass, or both. You just know there are rocks here somewhere—if only you could get at them.

The area near Crockett is a favorite for palm wood hunters. Pieces of variable sizes have been found along the roadsides. But bring your rake (leave the tiller at home please). Even at the areas where erosion has washed away some of the plant material, a rake may come in handy to unearth pieces of the sought-after wood.

Much of the wood presents a weathered exterior, hence the necessity for water. Wetting the suspects can often help distinguish the keepers from the throw-backs. Look for some nice red jasper in this area also.

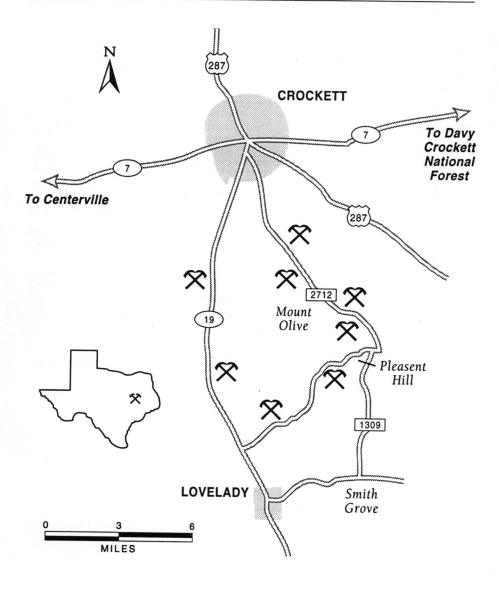

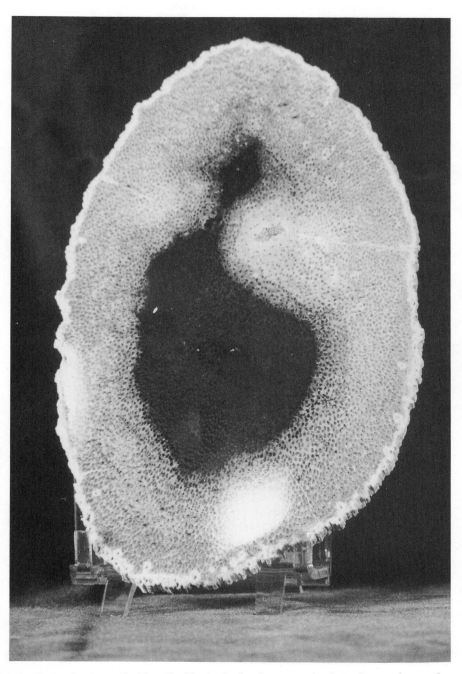

Petrified palm is easily identified by its lack of concentric rings that make up the vascular systems of other types of trees.

SITE 60 *LAKE SAM RAYBURN WOOD*

Land type: Pine forest.

Elevation: 328 feet.

Best season: Any.

Land manager: US Army Corps of Engineers.

Material: Petrified wood.

Tools: None.

Vehicle: Any.

Accommodations: RV parking and motels around lake.

Special attraction: Fishing.

Restrictions: Permission to collect must be obtained at the park entrance, and is limited to very small quantities.

For more information: Camping reservations for San Augustine Park may be made by calling 1-800-284-2267.

Finding the site: Sam Rayburn Reservoir is located in far East Texas, east of Lufkin. Most of the lake is encompassed within the Angelina National Forest. San Augustine Park on the north shore of the southeast end of the lake offers collecting outside the national forest. To get to the park travel south on U.S. Highway 96, 4.7 miles from the town of San Augustine. Turn east on Farm Road 1751. This road ends at the park entrance, about 18.5 miles after the turn.

Rockhounding: Pebbles of petrified wood, including palm wood, litter the sandy shores of this immense lake. The quality varies, but some of the pieces will tumble nicely, revealing good color. An occasional larger piece is possible as well. Don't overlook the possibility of finding Lower Tertiary fossils here also.

Though most of the other camping areas surrounding the lake are operated by the USDA Forest Service, San Augustine Park is operated by the U.S. Army Corps of Engineers. Its policy is to prohibit the taking of any material from the park without prior permission. Provided you plan to take only a handful or two of rocks, permission can be granted at the entrance gate by the park attendant.

If you're looking for a quiet camping getaway to do a little fishing, a little rock hunting, and a lot of relaxing, this place is for you. The park offers one hundred camping sites, all for a resonable fee, with water and electricity hookups, restrooms with showers, a sandy swimming beach, boat ramps, and a playground. The towering pines provide shade from the summer sun, and the scenery is guaranteed to soothe away your everyday stress.

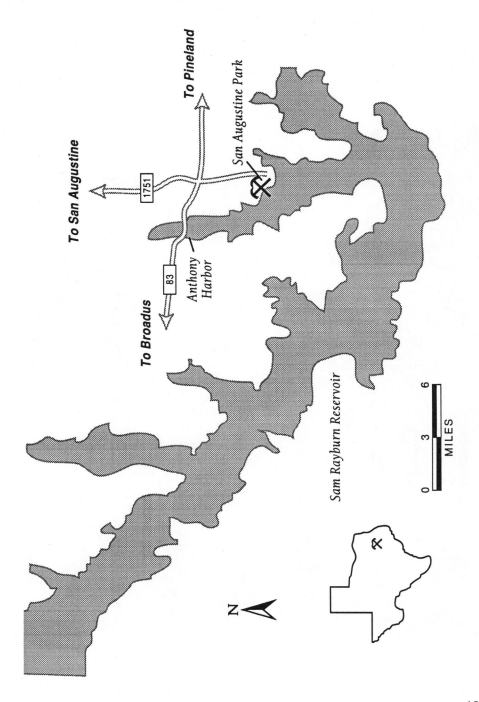

The shores of Sam Rayburn Reservoir are littered with petrified wood pebbles.

SITE 61 *NEWTON COUNTY WOOD AND FLINT*

Land type: Pine forest.

Elevation: 221 feet.

Best season: Early spring, late summer.

Land manager: Texas Department of Transportation.

Material: Wood, flint.

Tools: None.

Vehicle: Any.

Accommodations: RV parking and motels at either Sam Rayburn Reservoir, or Toledo Bend Reservoir.

Special attractions: Fishing.

Finding the site: Newton County is located in far East Texas along the Louisiana border, south of Toledo Bend Reservoir. Good collecting is found in areas of erosion along Recreation Road 255, which connects the dams of Sam Rayburn Reservoir and Toledo Bend Reservoir. Look also for any areas of recent road construction or oil drilling operations near the road, both of which disturb the surface plant material and expose previously hidden rocks. At the time of writing, good collecting was found at the intersection of RR 255 and Texas Highway 87.

Rockhounding: Though the pickings may often be small scale, any opportunity to collect in this region can potentially produce a quality piece of wood. The site at the intersection of RR 255 and TX 87 produced several small pieces of palm wood, one with very nice color. Also found here were pieces of gray flint, some showing signs of chipping and flaking at the edges. Thus arrowheads should not be ruled out as a possibility in the area.

More industrious collectors may wish to take along rakes or shovels to try their hand at discovering buried treasure at sites where no erosion is present. This approach could yield a sizable cache, but care should be taken to not add to the battle with erosion fought by the Department of Transportation. Refill all holes, and replace sod.

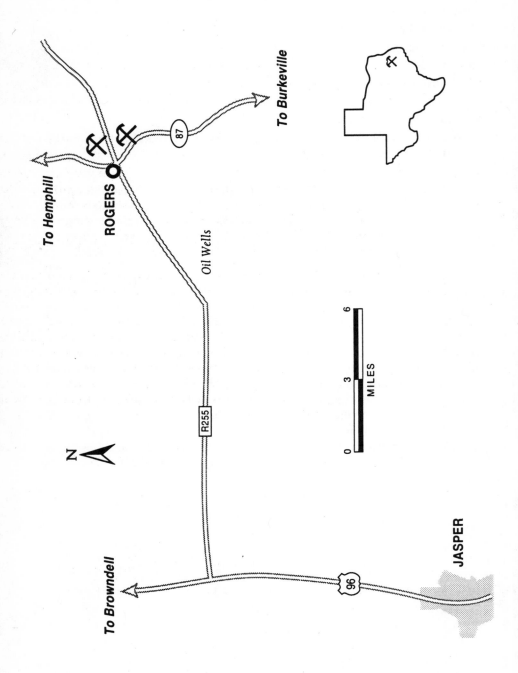

SITE 62 *SABINE RIVER WOOD*

Land type: Pine forest.

Elevation: 221 feet.

Best season: Early spring, late summer.

Land manager: Sabine River Authority.

Material: Petrified wood, some palm wood.

Tools: Rock pick, shovel.

Vehicle: Any.

Accommodations: RV parking and motels around lake.

Special attraction: Fishing.

Finding the site: Toledo Bend Reservoir is centered on the eastern border of the state. The dam is located at the southern end of the lake. Collecting is allowed on either side of the Sabine River below the dam. Travel east on Farm Road 692, until it reaches the dam. From FR 692 turn south onto a dirt road which parallels the river. Travel several hundred feet to safe parking.

Rockhounding: Though collecting of petrified wood is a somewhat speculative adventure throughout most of East Texas, the Sabine River has quite effectively cut through the lush growth and topsoil to expose some of the best wood available in the area.

That's the good news. The bad news is that the area below the dam has been known to collectors for years and is therefore quite worked over in terms of pieces large enough for cutting. Sharp-eyed collectors who don't mind getting a little muddy after a rain shower will be the most successful here. The rain often exposes new pieces in the muddy embankments, and rinses clean previously exposed treasures.

That is not to say that collectors seeking small stones won't find wood here. There are plenty of fragments to be had, in various qualities. Even amongst the tiniest slices of river-worn wood, there are jewels to be found. It simply takes patience and careful examination of every piece of wood.

Try washing or scratching the weathered surface to determine if there is a colorful gem waiting inside. With quantities so plentiful, it is also wise to take a few of the pieces that you deem less than beautiful. Often a simple change of lighting is all that is required to reveal the true character of the stone.

Caution is advised here. The banks of the river are steep and slippery. The area is also prone to flooding, so never attempt to collect during a rain storm.

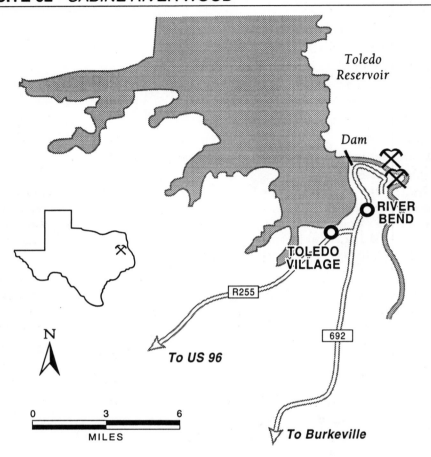

SITE 63 *TRINITY COUNTY PALM WOOD*

Land type: Pine forest.

Elevation: 350 feet.

Best season: Early spring, late summer.

Land manager: Texas Department of Transportation.

Material: Petrified wood.

Tools: Rake, shovel, rock pick.

Vehicle: Any.

Accommodations: RV parking and motels within 5 miles.

Special attraction: Fishing, Johnson's Rock Shop.

Finding the site: Trinity County is located approximately eighty-nine miles north of Houston. The town of Trinity is at the western edge of the county, at the junction of Texas Highways 19 and 94. From Trinity travel east on FR 356. Look for any area of erosion that might expose the rocks. Another route to try is north toward Crockett on TX 96.

Rockhounding: Break out the rake again. There's wood here, and lots of it. Small pieces are the normal roadside find, but even football-sized pieces have been unearthed along TX 96. The problem is simply getting to it. Any area where rocks are exposed at the surface should be carefully examined. When no such areas can be found, try creating a little exposure yourself. It can be hard work, but the results are usually worth it.

SITE 63 TRINITY COUNTY PALM WOOD

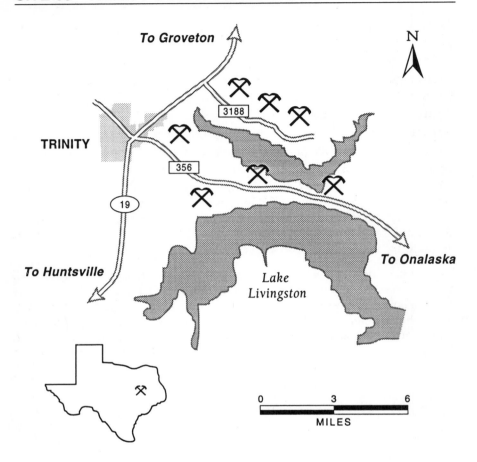

To Groveton

N

3188

TRINITY

356

19

To Huntsville

To Onalaska

Lake
Livingston

0 3 6

MILES

SITE 64 *LIVINGSTON AREA WOOD*

Land type: Forest.

Elevation: 194 feet.

Best season: Early spring, late summer.

Land manager: Private.

Material: Petrified wood.

Tools: Shovel, rock pick, pry bars.

Vehicle: Any.

Accommodations: RV parking and motels in Livingston.

Special attraction: Gem and mineral collection at Houston Museum of Natural Science.

For more information: Contact the Johnson Rock Shop at 409-563-4438. The number for the Houston Museum of Natural Science is 713-639-4613.

Finding the site: For detailed information on private property collecting in the Livingston area (and most of East Texas), a visit to Johnson's Rock Shop in Indian Springs is necessary. Indian Springs is located on U.S. Highway 190 about ten miles east of Livingston. Turn south at the Indian Springs Store. Turn left at the first street, then right, and then left again. This puts you on Ole Don Road. From there travel about three-quarters of a mile to

Logs of petrified palm wood, like these found at the Johnson Rockshop, can still be found in some areas.

139

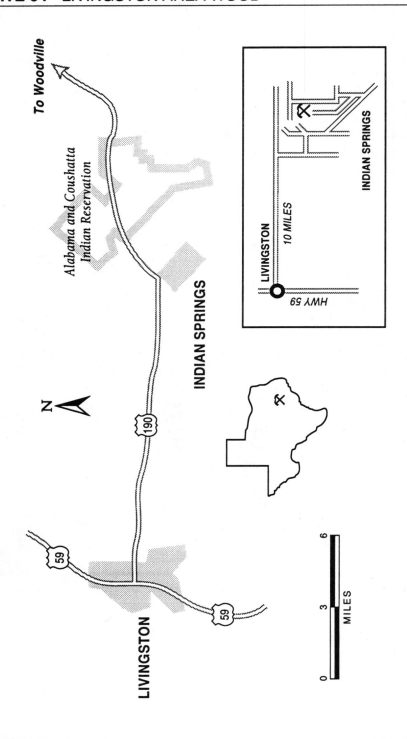

Flanagan Street. Turn left. Zigzag left, then right to Wiggins St. The rock shop is on the left about 0.1 mile after the turn.

Rockhounding: Please don't let the complicated directions keep you from visiting this wonderful shop. You will have missed out on an opportunity to see the state's premier collection of petrified wood and a chat with one of the state's most knowledgeable rockhounds.

Otis Johnson is quite the celebrity. He and his shop have been featured in numerous publications, and on television more than once. But none of that seems important to Mr. Johnson. What is important are the rocks. He loves to talk rocks. He'll trade stories with any one who drops by. (He's got the proof to back up his tales all around him.) There are pieces of wood in his back yard so large that logging trucks were required just to bring them home.

Ask him anything. He is a virtual font of information on slabbing, cabbing, and tumbling. He'll even show you how he designed and built his tumbler. His latest project is creating stone-encrusted concrete sections for use in landscaping. He'll show you how if you're interested.

If you are looking for a good place to collect anywhere near here, just tell him what you hope to find, and he'll point you in the right direction. On a good day, he just might take you there himself.

While you're this close, visit the second-best rock collection in the state at the Houston Museum of Natural Science. (It's second to the Johnson collection because it isn't composed of native rocks.) Read through the introduction section titled, "Sights to See" for more detailed information on the collection.

SOUTH TEXAS

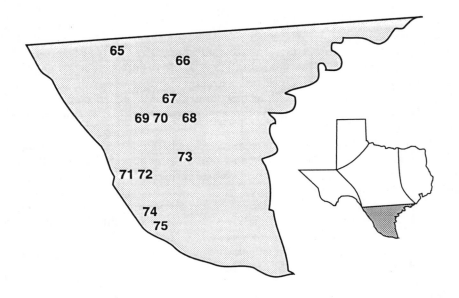

OVERVIEW

Agate and wood are the primary goals for this region. The agate is usually clear with colorful inclusions randomly swirled throughout. Much of the material is a simple clear and white. The wood includes palm wood in small pieces. Some of the wood is well-agatized and colorful enough for cutting. Gray flint and brightly colored jasper are also quite common in the region.

Roadside collecting is excellent here. Sandy embankments present ideal places to search. Some collecting also is possible around lakes and rivers. Choke Canyon Reservoir, which was formerly a popular collecting area, is now encompassed within a state park. But the shores of Falcon Reservoir (other than inside the state park) still offer some of the best agate collecting in the state.

In most cases, where collecting is limited to roadsides, winter is the ideal season for collecting in the southern region of the state. Temperatures are mild and the huge snake population spends most of the time in hibernation. Spring collecting is also quite pleasant. In contrast, summer temperatures can be unbearable.

There should be some concern about game hunting in the area. Any collecting on or adjacent to private property should be scheduled around deer and turkey seasons. There is often an extended season on deer in some southern counties, so check with the Texas Parks and Wildlife Department for their annual publication that lists seasons by county. It should be availlable at any retailer where hunting supplies are sold.

SITE 65 *DEVINE CHOCOLATE AGATE*

Land type: Rolling plains.

Elevation: 670 feet.

Best season: Late summer.

Land manager: Texas Department of Transportation.

Material: Agate and flint.

Tools: None.

Vehicle: Any.

Accommodations: RV parking and motels within 5 miles.

Special attractions: San Antonio area attractions.

Finding the site: Devine is located just off of Interstate 35, thirty-two miles southwest of San Antonio. From Devine travel north on Texas Highway 173. At about 4.2 miles north of town, there is a rocky road cut on the west side of the road.

Rockhounding: It is quite possible that the founders of this tiny town spelled the name of the town wrong, because in terms of rocks, the stuff here is simply divine. Pebbles and cobbles of rich brown flint and agate litter the hillside. Many are weathered and present rough white or tan exteriors, so look carefully for tell-tale signs of what is hidden inside.

The majority of the material qualifies as flint due to overall lack of clarity, but the color and texture is that of smooth milk chocolate. The agate is the same deep brown, and occasionally bears lighter-colored inclusions. Both materials should cut and polish much the same as any other chalcedony-based rock. The author plans to tumble many of the smaller pieces, creating a bowl of bonbons to display on the coffee table, but there is no limit to the imaginative uses for this deliciously colored material.

SITE 65 *DEVINE CHOCOLATE AGATE*

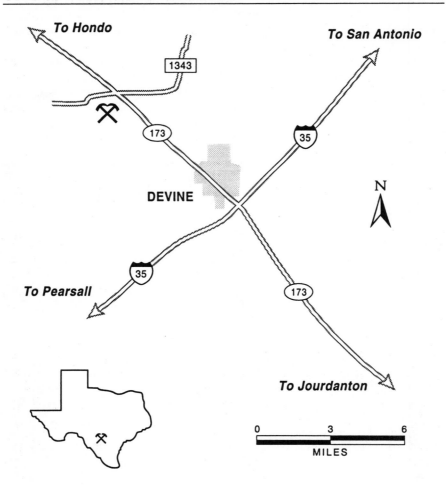

To Hondo

To San Antonio

1343

173

35

DEVINE

N

35

173

To Pearsall

To Jourdanton

0   3   6
MILES

SITE 66 *FALLS CITY AGATE AND WOOD*

Land type: Rolling plains.

Elevation: 525 feet.

Best season: Winter, spring.

Land manager: Texas Department of Transportation.

Material: Agate, wood, onyx.

Tools: Shovel.

Vehicle: Any.

Accommodations: RV parking and motels within 30 miles.

Special attractions: San Antonio area attractions.

Finding the site: Falls City is located on U.S. Highway 181 about forty-three miles south of San Antonio. From Falls City travel west on Farm Road 791. Good collecting begins about two miles from town, and continues for almost five miles. Look for areas of erosion and outcroppings of limestone.

Rockhounding: The area surrounding this tiny town is ideal for collecting an interesting mix of wood, agate, flint, and onyx. Most of the wood is colorful and well-agatized, some of the best in the state in fact. Look for agate that is snow-white with either black dendrites or green moss inclusions. Also keep a sharp eye out for flint that has been worked.

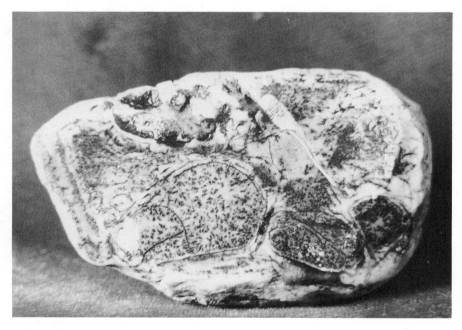

White and black agate is found near Falls City.

SITE 66 *FALLS CITY AGATE AND WOOD*

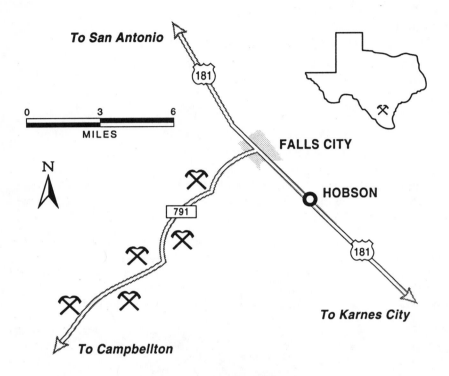

The agate and related chalcedony-based materials found throughout this region is almost entirely float material. Most likely it was formed as veins and nodules in limestone beds laid down during the Lower Tertiary time period (37-66 million years ago). The softer limestone and sandstone eroded away, leaving the chalcedony.

The size of the pieces varies considerably here. The wood can be pinkie-sized slivers, or grapefruit-sized chunks. The agate is generally in small pebbles or cobbles, but never overlook the possibility of a larger piece.

Collectors looking for small pieces suitable for tumbling will not be disappointed here. When tumbling the white agate, keep in mind that it is slightly softer than other agates, requiring considerably less time for shaping. Frequent checks should eliminate the possibility of melting away all the good stuff.

SITE 67 CAMPBELLTON SELENITE

Land type: Plains.

Elevation: 374 feet.

Best season: Winter, spring.

Land manager: Texas Department of Transportation.

Material: Selenite, agate, jasper, wood.

Tools: None.

Vehicle: Any.

Accommodations: RV parking and motels within 20 miles.

Special attraction: Choke Canyon Reservoir.

Finding the site: Campbellton is located on Interstate 37, about fifty-four miles south of San Antonio. In Campbellton take U.S. Highway 281A, which branches off of I-37/US 281 to the south. Look for gypsum beds in the road cuts beginning about 5.5 miles from town.

Rockhounding: Nicely formed selenite crystals twinkle in the sunlight from the roadsides near Campbellton. While there are plenty of slivers to choose from all along this stretch of highway look for crystals, which are twinned, or are grouped in bunches. They may be somewhat difficult to find, but worth the extra effort.

There are also small jasper pebbles here, as well as, petrified wood that is high in silica content and often colorful. Don't overlook the possibility of agates lurking in the loose gypsum. If your heart is set on agates, however, don't spend a great deal of time here. There are much better sites just down the road.

SITE 67   *CAMPBELLTON SELENITE*

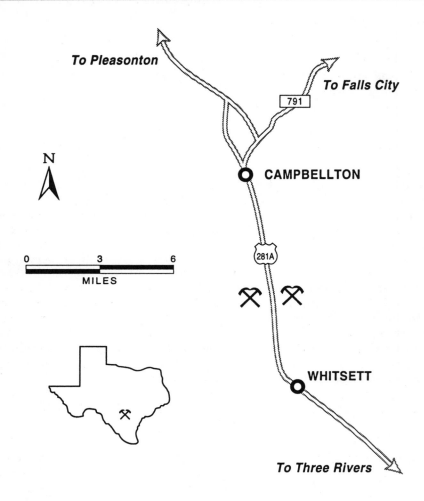

SITE 68 *THREE RIVERS AGATE*

Land type: Plains.

Elevation: 145 feet.

Best season: Winter, spring.

Land manager: Texas Department of Transportation.

Material: Agate, wood, and jasper.

Tools: Shovel.

Vehicle: Any.

Accommodations: RV parking at Choke Canyon Reservoir, motels in Three Rivers.

Special attractions: Fishing, Corpus Christi

Restrictions: No collecting is allowed in Choke Canyon State Park.

Finding the site: Three Rivers is located just off Interstate 37, about seventy-nine miles south of San Antonio. From Three Rivers travel west on Texas Highway 72. Good collecting begins about four miles from town and continues for four or five miles. Look for rocky areas along the roadsides.

Rockhounding: The area surrounding Choke Canyon Reservoir has long been known by agate hunters. Because the lake is now encompassed by a state park, collecting is off limits. Small pebbles of various colors are still collectible along TX 72, though.

Careful inspection of the loose rocks found at the surface is required because they are heavily weathered. Expect mostly clear agates with colorful inclusions, but don't rule out white, green, gold, or red.

The wood here is the same as much of the material found throughout South Texas, small to medium-sized pieces, with good silica content and color.

From Three Rivers, it is a short drive (seventy-one miles) south on I-37 to Corpus Christi. Though the rock collecting opportunities are slim, the city offers a great many other activities. Gulf fishing is available either on chartered boats or from enormous piers. For those who love learning about the world under the sea there is the Texas State Aquarium. There are historical homes, art museums, and of course, miles of beaches to explore.

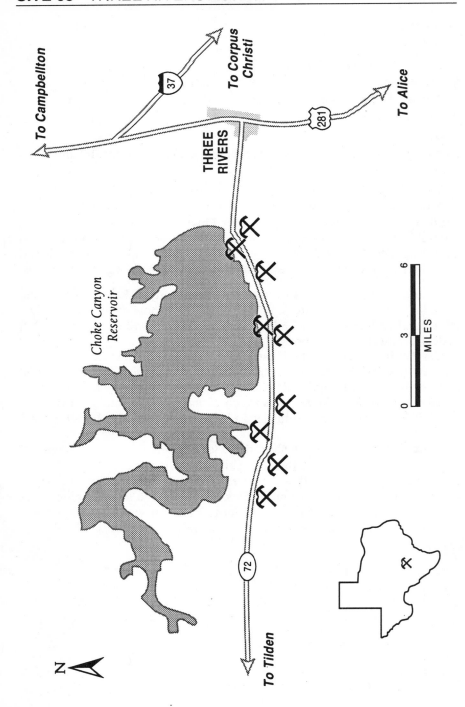

SITE 69 *FRIO RIVER WOOD*

Land type: Plains.

Elevation: 145 feet.

Best season: Any.

Land manager: Texas Department of Transportation.

Material: Petrified wood.

Tools: Rock pick, water.

Vehicle: Any.

Accommodations: RV parking at Choke Canyon Reservoir, motels in Three Rivers.

Special attraction: Fishing.

Finding the site: Good collecting of petrified wood is found along the Frio River as it passes through the town of Tilden, west of Choke Canyon Reservoir. In Tilden travel west through town on Texas Highway 72. After the road crosses the river, there is a dirt road to the east that allows access to the area below the bridge. The wood is most plentiful on the road itself, rather than the river banks.

Rockhounding: This area has perhaps one of the most plentiful supplies of small wood pieces in the state. Almost every step along the road leading down to the river places your foot in contact with petrified wood. Much of it is palm wood. Be aware that the smaller pieces make identificaiton more difficult. The xylem and phloem tubes are tiny, and sometimes aren't noticed until the piece is cut or polished. Look for pieces that are black, gray, or a combination of the two.

Sizable pieces of other woods are plentiful, and many are large enough for cabbing. Qualities vary consiserably, so washing is recommended to help determine potential, though many will not show their true colors until cut and polished.

When sorting through the wood at this site, there are a couple of things to keep in mind to help find a few really good pieces. Weight can be a very good indicator in determining the quality of a piece of wood. The heavier a piece feels in the hand, the more likely it is to have a high silica content, and thus produce a fine cut stone. Some hounds also swear by sound. The poor quality pieces produce a hollow or dull sound when clinked with another stone, whereas well agatized wood produces a tinkling sound.

Whether the stones here are music to your ears or not take along a rock pick for prying lose those stubborn pieces stuck just below the surface. The ground here is very hard. There is little evidence, however, of large pieces buried deeper than an inch or two, so a shovel won't likely be necessary.

SITE 69 *FRIO RIVER WOOD*
SITE 70 *TILDEN AGATE*

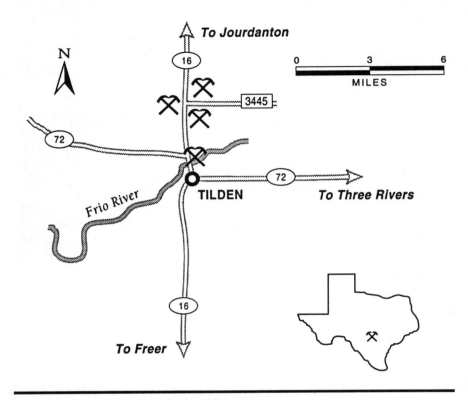

SITE 70 *TILDEN AGATE*

Land type: Plains.

Elevation: 145 feet.

Best season: Winter, spring.

Land manager: Texas Department of Transportation.

Material: Agate, flint, petrified wood.

Tools: None.

Vehicle: Any.

Accommodations: RV parking at Choke Canyon Reservoir, motels in Three Rivers.

Special attraction: Fishing.

Restrictions: No collecting is allowed at Choke Canyon State Park.

Finding the site: Tilden is located at the west end of Choke Canyon Reservoir at the intersection of Texas highways 16 and 72. It is about sixty-eight

Petrified wood found near the Frio River.

miles south of San Antonio. From Tilden travel north on TX 16. Good collecting begins approximately 3.1 miles north of town and continues for roughly four miles.

Rockhounding: The same material found along the southern edge of Choke Canyon Reservoir along TX 72 can be found north of Tilden, as TX 16 passes the lake area. Look for slightly higher concentrations of petrified wood here, however.

While your efforts may be concentrated on finding agates or good wood specimens don't fail to examine flint chips in this area as well. There is a good deal of worked material. Though most of it is scrap, good arrowhead specimens are always possible.

SITE 71 *NORTH LAREDO AGATE*

Land type: Hills.
Elevation: 438 feet.
Best season: Winter, spring.
Land manager: Texas Department of Transportation.
Material: Agate, wood.

Tools: shovel, rock pick, water.

Vehicle: Any.

Accommodations: Numerous motels and hotels in Laredo.

Special attraction: Shopping in Nuevo Laredo.

Finding the site: Laredo is at the southern end of Interstate 35, where it meets the Mexican border. It is about 155 miles southwest of San Antonio. From I-35 entering Laredo exit onto Farm Road 3464, about 3.6 miles south of the northern city limit. Go 1.5 miles to Farm Road 1472. This road is also known as Mines Road. Because this is an extremely busy road that is heavily traveled by international trucking companies, safe collecting is not possible for approximately 10.4 miles.

Rockhounding: If you stop along I-35 as you near Laredo, your anticipation will begin to build. Roadside parks along the way often bear tiny samples of the goodies to come as you travel south. The area around Laredo is ripe with agates in all colors and sizes.

The material is entirely float, presents a very weathered exterior, and is often difficult to distinguish from lesser quality chert material. But don't let any of that stop you. The good stuff is here; it just takes a careful eye.

Look for white fortification agates, clear blue, and colorless with vivid gold and yellow splashes. The agates here come in all sizes, so don't limit yourself to looking at only the small rocks (or the large ones either). The best white fortification piece collected here by the author was fist-sized, but a marble-sized clear stone with a brown and gold bullseye found here is a definite show stopper even if it is small.

Don't overlook the wood here. It isn't found in large quantities, but what is available is good cutting quality. While you're busy looking for rocks don't forget to keep one eye looking for rattlesnakes.

Anytime the temperature rises above 65 degrees (which would be a normal occurrence in winter here), the little devils are likely to be about. The author received a timely reminder to use caution here. As a stone was lifted for closer inspection, a rattler skeleton was revealed beneath it. He was just a little guy, but one little rattlesnake is all it takes.

When you're through gathering treasure, and avoiding snakes, this is an excellent place to sample some south-of-the-border shopping. Nuevo Laredo is quite an experience. There are bargains on clothing, glassware, art, and some great rockhounding hats. A word of caution: don't take any rocks across the border with you in your vehicle. They can be confiscated by the U.S. Department of Agriculture when you return. The concern is apparently due to soil-born diseases like swine cholera.

If you don't have any place to leave your rocks while you venture into Mexico stop at the customs clearance area before crossing the border to show them what you are taking with you.

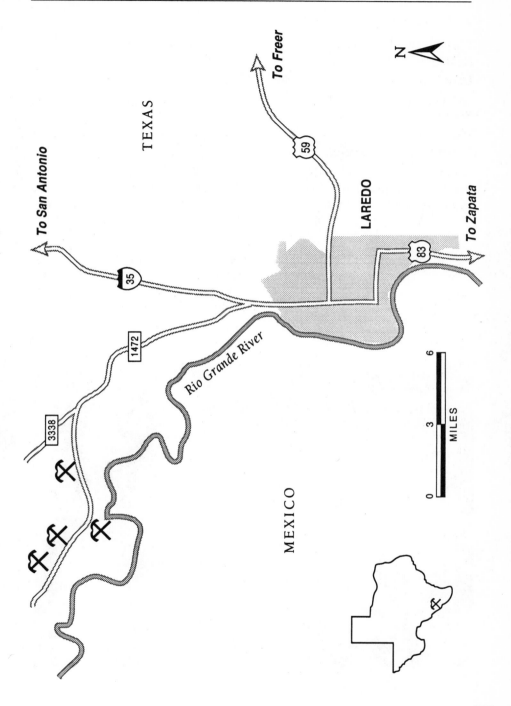

SITE 72 *SOUTH LAREDO AGATE*

Land type: Hills.

Elevation: 438 feet.

Best season: Winter, spring.

Land manager: Texas Department of Transportation.

Material: Agate.

Tools: Shovel.

Vehicle: Any.

Accommodations: Numerous hotels and motels in Laredo.

Special attractions: Shopping in Nuevo Laredo, Mexico.

Finding the Site: Laredo is at the southern end of Interstate 35, where it meets the Mexican border. It is about 155 miles southwest of San Antonio. From Laredo take U.S. Highway 83 south. Good collecting begins approximately eight miles south of town.

Rockhounding: The material found here will be essentially the same as that found north of town. Look for agates hiding behind very weathered exteriors, in various sizes and colors. Not every stop along the road will produce good pieces. If your first site seems to be a dud simply move a little farther down the road.

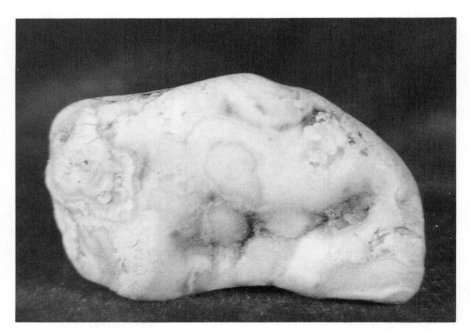

White agate found north of Laredo.

SITE 72 *SOUTH LAREDO AGATE*

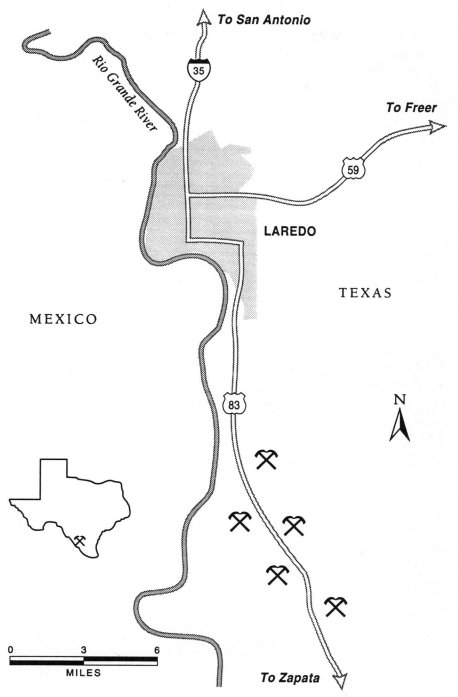

SITE 73 *FREER AGATE*

Land type: Hills.

Elevation: 158 feet.

Best season: Winter, spring.

Land manager: Texas Department of Transportation.

Material: Agate, wood.

Tools: Shovel.

Vehicle: Any.

Accommodations: Motels in Freer.

Special attractions: None.

Finding the site: Freer is located at the intersection of U.S. Highway 59 and Texas Highway 16. It is about 109 miles south of San Antonio, and 65 miles northeast of Laredo. From Freer travel approximately nineteen miles south on TX 16. Look for a rocky road cut on both sides of the road. This road cut appears suddenly after miles of chalky white cuts bearing no agate whatsoever.

Rockhounding: Though not found in large quantities, the quality of the agates found at this remote site is quite surprising. Look chiefly for white banded material. Some of the same clear agate bearing brown or gold balls is also found here. As is the case with most collecting in this region, the stones are heavily weathered. There are also small quantities of petrified wood here, some of it palm wood.

Freer is located in the heart of a deer hunting region, so care should be taken to avoid private property from November through the end of January. Check with the Texas Parks and Wildlife Department for specific information regarding season dates.

SITE 73 *FREER AGATE*

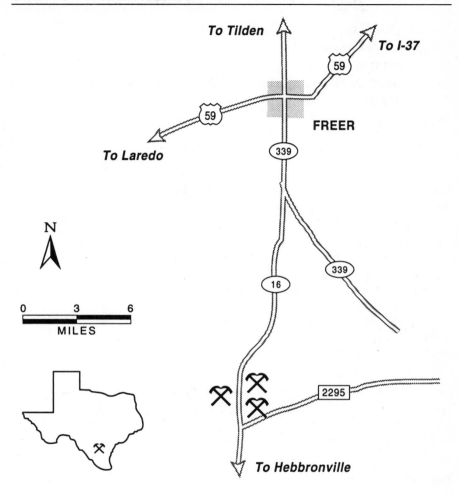

SITE 74 *AGATE NORTH OF ZAPATA*

Land type: Hills.
Elevation: 311 feet.
Best season: Winter, spring.
Land manager: Texas Department of Transportation.
Material: Agate.
Tools: None.
Vehicle: Any.
Accommodations: RV parking and motels in Zapata.
Special attraction: Fishing.
Finding the site: Zapata is located near the Mexican border on U.S. Highway 83, approximately forty-nine miles south of Laredo. In Zapata take U.S. 83 north 5.9 miles to a roadside picnic area overlooking Falcon Reservoir.

Rockhounding: This is a site designed purely to whet your appetite for the collecting to come. The ground surrounding this scenic overlook is covered with tiny agates suitable for tumbling. The good part is that they are not as weathered as those found along the shores of the lake. This makes them easier to spot amongst the other pebbles.

The collector looking for tumbling material may in fact be quite satisfied with the take here and not feel the need to move on. If larger stones are your forte, though, look a little then move on to Site 75, Falcon Reservoir Agate and Wood.

SITE 75 *FALCON RESERVOIR AGATE AND WOOD*

Land type: Lake shore.
Elevation: 311 feet.
Best season: Winter, spring.
Land manager: Falcon Reservoir Water Authority.
Material: Agate.
Tools: Rock pick, water.
Vehicle: Any.
Accommodations: RV parking at the lake, motels in Zapata.
Special attraction: Fishing.
Restrictions: No collecting is permitted within the state park.
Finding the site: International Falcon Reservoir is located along the Mexican border about forty-fives mile south of Laredo. Good collecting can be found almost anywhere along the shores of the lake. Of particular interest is a site west of Zapata. From Zapata travel west on Farm Road 496 approxi-

SITE 74 *AGATE NORTH OF ZAPATA*
SITE 75 *FALCON RESERVOIR AGATE AND WOOD*

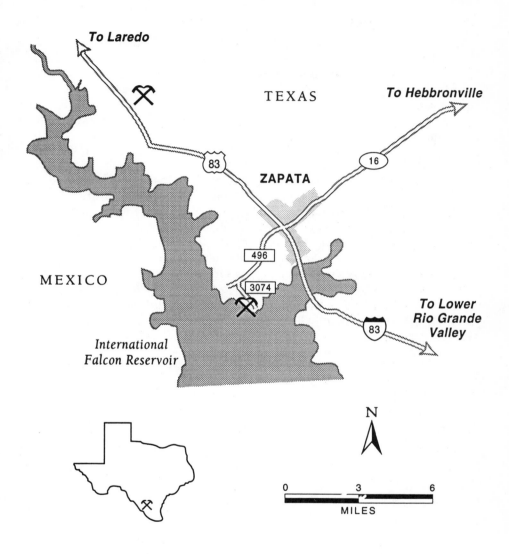

mately 3.3 miles to Farm Road 3074. Turn south and travel on this road until the pavement ends. Just beyond the pavement is a public boat ramp. Turn right, away from the boat ramp, toward a retaining wall built with large boulders. Collecting is very good from the retaining wall to the water's edge.

Rockhounding: Hopefully all good rockhounds will end up some place like this when they pass on, because this is truly agate heaven. There are more agates here than one hound could pick up in a lifetime. Like most good collecting sites however, there is one little catch. The rocks are very heavily coated with mud from the lake, and it doesn't wash off easily.

This makes sorting the good from the not-so-good an almost impossible task onsite. Take along water to use on the few pieces you find that aren't covered with the armor-like mud. Be prepared to take home lots of rocks in order to do a more thorough cleaning job at home. Some of the smaller pieces are best cleaned by a short spell in the tumbler with eighty-pound grit. Larger pieces may simply have to be cut to reveal the treasure within.

The agates here are usually a clear smoky color, with vivid inclusions of gold, orange, brown, black, white, and an occasional green. Most have random swirls, but a few pieces will exhibit thistle, moss, or fortification patterns. Don't be surprised however, once you've cleaned your prizes to find some with no color at all, just clear gray. This is all the more reason to take home plenty so that you won't be disappointed by a lack of color.

In your rush to get at the agates don't overlook the astounding assortment of wood. The author collected more palm wood here than at any other site in the state. Most of it is typically gray and black, but a few pieces will exhibit deep blue, red, or orange.

GLOSSARY

Agate: A banded or variegated chalcedony.

Agatized: Impregnated with silicon dioxide, producing a secondary material that is banded or variegated.

Alabaster: A very fine-grained variety of gypsum.

Bouquet agate: Multi-colored agate bearing flower-like inclusions.

Brachiopods: Members of a small phylum of marine animals with bivalve shells similar to oysters and clams.

Bryozoans: Members of the phylum Bryozoa of aquatic animals. They have a tubular body, generally with a sponge-like texture.

Cabbing: The act of creating a cabochon.

Cabochon: A stone shaped into a convex curve and polished, but left unfaceted.

Calcite: Calcium carbonate; often in clear crystals.

Carnelian: A dark red to orange translucent variety of chalcedony.

Casting: A fossil created when the impression left by a living plant or animal is filled with another material.

Celestite: Crystals of strontium sulfate.

Cephalopod: A member of the marine animal class cephalopoda. Includes nautiluses and ammonites.

Chalcedony: A microcrystalline form of quartz (silicon dioxide). Varieties include agate, carnelian, onyx, flint, jasper, chrysoprase, and heliotrope.

Chert: A sedimentary rock composed chiefly of silicon dioxide. Often confused with chalcedony. Chert contains inpurities, making it opaque, slightly dull, and less colorful. Some flints are actually chert, rather than the purer chalcedony.

Chrysoprase: An apple-green translucent to opaque form of chalcedony.

Cinnabar: Mercuric sulfide. Bright red in color; forms in crystalline or granular varieties.

Crinoid: A member of the large aquatic animal class crinoidea. Consists of tubular bodies composed of stacked "buttons," crowned by five or more feathery arms.

Dendrites: Tree-like inclusions of one mineral in another.

Dike: A thin vertical deposit of lava (usually basaltic), which cuts upwards through existing horizontal rock layers. A similar deposit of lava but between horizontal rock layers, is a "sill."

Dolomite: Calcium magnesium carbonate. Possible in both crystalline and granular varieties.

Echinoids: Sea urchins and sand dollars; members of the marine animal class echinoidea.

Feldspar: Any of a group of very common rock-forming silicate minerals.

Flint: An opaque variety of chalcedony or chert, in colors including gray, black, brown, white, or red.

Float: Rock material found in a location other than that in which it originally formed.

Fortification agate: Multi-colored agate bearing swirls or banding of alternating colors that follow the shape of the rock.

Fossil: The remains or impressions of once-living things from the remote geological past.

Gad: A pointed tool used for loosening or breaking rock.

Galena: Lead sulfide; presenting cubic cleavage. Usually silver-gray.

Gastropods: A member of the largest class of mollusks, Gastropoda, including snails.

Geode: A hollow rock nodule, often lined with crystals.

Globular: Formed in rounded masses, resembling a bunch of grapes.

Granite: Medium-to-fine grained rock normally composed of feldspar, quartz, and mica.

Graptolites: Any of several extinct marine organisms fossilized as imprints in Paleozoic shale.

Grossular: A variety of garnet; can be colorless, white, yellow, pink, green or brown.

Hematite: Iron oxide. Can occur in massive forms, as black crystals, or as a red powder.

Igneous: Rock formed by the cooling of molten material.

Inclusion: One mineral enclosed within another.

Jasper: A variegated, mottled, opaque form of chalcedony in colors of red, yellow, or brown.

Labradorite: Multi-colored variety of feldspar.

Limonite: A mixture of hydrous iron oxides.

Lower Cretaceous: The first half of the Cretaceous period, 66-144 million years ago.

Lower Tertiary: The first half of the Tertiary period, 37-66 million years ago.

Manganite: Manganese oxide; steel gray to black crystals.

Matrix: The dirt or rock in which a fossil is embedded.

Metamorphic: Rocks that have undergone a noticeable change in character or chemical make-up due to extreme heat, pressure, or both.

Mica: Any of a group of silicate minerals formed in thin sheets.

Microcrystalline: Having crystals visible only through a microscope.

Missisippian: Period of the Paleozoic era, lasting from 320 to 360 million years ago.

Mohs Scale: A scale of hardness for rating minerals, one (talc) being the softest, and ten (diamond) the hardest.

Onyx: Banded, opaque variety of chalcedony, usually in colors of red, white, and golden tan.

Opal: An amorphous form of hydrous silica, often with a deep play of color (fire).

Paleocene: Epoch in the Tertiary period, 58 to 66 million years ago.

Pegmatite: Course-grained variety of granite.

Pennsylvanian: Period in the Paleozoic era, 286-320 million years ago.

Phloem: The food conducting tubes of a plant's vascular system.

Pictographs: A drawing on rock used to represent a thing or idea.

Plume agate: A variety of agate characterized by single-color inclusions of tree-like formations.

Pom Pom agate: An agate variety with colorful circles or balls of another color.

Prase: See chrysoprase.

Quartzite: Rock in which quartz is the predominate mineral.

Schist: Medium- to coarse-grained metamorphic rock with prominent parallel mineral orientation.

Sedimentary: Rock formed by the compaction and cementation of fragments of other rocks or living creatures, or by the precipitation of material from a solution.

Selenite: Colorless, transparent gypsum crystals.

Specific gravity: Relative weight of any substance. Specific gravities are given numbers comparing the weight of one substance to that of an equal volume of water. Example: a mineral with a specific gravity of two is twice as heavy as water.

Streak plate: A white, unglazed tile, used to identify minerals based on the color they leave when scraped on the tile.

Stringers: Small vein-like inclusions of one mineral running through another mineral or rock.

Tektite: A rounded, glassy rock. Probably of meteoric origin.

Tertiary: Period of the Cenozoic era, 2-66 million years ago.

Trilobite: Member of the extinct class of marine arthropods trilobita.

Turritella : Genus of long, slender snails.

Upper Cretaceous: The second half of the Cretaceous period, 66-144 million years ago.

Uvarovite: Emerald-green variety of garnet.

Vein: A mineral deposit clearly separated from the rock around it.

Xylem: Water and mineral conducting channels in a plant's vascular system.

ABOUT THE AUTHOR

Melinda Crow is a free-lance journalist who's motto is "Never stop learning." Her research for her writing is the pefect means of accomplishing that. Having grown up in Amarillo, she moved to Odessa in 1980. What she learned there was a deeper appreciation for the beauty of her home state. She and husband Gary spent every available weekend and vacation traveling in Central and West Texas.

This is her first book, but her work has appeared in magazines such as Texas Highways, National Gardening, 3-2-1 Contact, Parenting, and Successful Camping. While family-oriented travel writing is her specialty, there are no limits to the subjects she's willing to tackle.

She is a certified Texas Master Gardener, with special interests in Xeriscaping and native plant gardening. Her newly discovered love for rocks has inspired her to create a garden overflowing with plants and rocks native to Texas.

She recently moved back to Amarillo with husband Gary and daughter Alyssa. Together they are eagerly exploring the region of the state she took for granted while growing up.